Back to the Land...
for Self-Preservation

A Freedom, Life-style
and Nutritional Commentary

by
Dr. N.W. WALKER,
Doctor of Science.

"Two things have I required of thee; deny me them not before I die: Remove far from me vanity and lies; give me neither poverty nor riches; feed me with food convenient for me."

Proverbs 30: 7-8

Published by:

Norwalk PRESS

107 North Cortez, Suite 200
Prescott, Arizona 86301

Manufactured in the United States of America.

ISBN: 0-89019-063-1

Ninth Printing

Oh the joy of blue skies and pure air,
of the song of the birds for mirth,
Of a home in the country where
there is freedom from pressures and dearth,
To be nearer to God in a garden
than anywhere else on earth!

Norwalk PRESS

107 N. Cortez, Suite 200 / Prescott, Arizona 86301

Contents

1.
Live your Life with a Purpose

Read every word this book contains
And let your mind and thinking wander
'Neath skies of blue and gentle rains
Into the lovely country, yonder.   *N.W.W.*

What is the purpose of your being here on Earth? What does Mother Earth have in store for you? What can the lowly soil do for you?

A wise Minister once wrote: Only a few inches of top-soil separate us from death.

It is time to get back to THE LAND. Learn by other people's experiences and profit by their mistakes. Others have achieved success on their few acres of land, attaining independence and security. What others have done you, too, can do.

This book is by no means a "specialty item". It is written and intended for Y O U. Maybe . . . . by the time you're through reading this book you may have discovered the secret to attain peace while the heathen rage.

Are Y O U living YOUR life with a PURPOSE? How contented are you with your life?

Are you HAPPY and SATISFIED with the endless rush and stress of your daily activities?

Do you EVER long for EMANCIPATION?

What a blissful expression = EMANCIPATION! It · means RELEASE! It means to free a slave from bondage.

FREEDOM means the life you WANT to live. Freedom is to experience the full expression of your life—to Live Life with a PURPOSE!

Always be aware of the fact that Freedom carries with it great responsibility.

Do you know the thrill of lacy sunlight beams filtering through the trees at day-break, sunsets caressing the Western horizon or setting it aflame with a riot of breathtaking colors? Of lengthening shadows weaving dreamy fantasies into the very depth of the soul, of myriad twinkling lights of the constellations in the deepening indigo-blue sky of a crackling Winter's night?

Do you know the thrill of a warm wind drifting through aroma-laden atmospheres of new-mown hay, of breezes wandering from a wooded pinery or from the perfume-laden blossoms in an orchard, the heart-stirring redolent bouquet of the wild honeysuckle vines, the sweet fragrance of the Evening Primrose while strolling under the unbroken canopy of turquoise skies as days melt into twilight?

These are what Almighty God created with a PURPOSE. For Y O U !

Concrete and brick structures, cement sidewalks and asphalt pavements are produced by man. What do THEY do? They serve to encase mass throngs of a heterogeneous humanity, existing with no destination except their daily treadmill.

Far too many, deluded and misguided, are beguiled into a maelstrom of Metropolitan City life, not realizing nor appreciating what their Creator established for their benefit at birth in the country atmosphere which they deserted.

More and more men and women are moving away from the pressures and delusions of life in the Metropolitan City to find Vibrant Health for their body, peace for their mind, a renewing of Life and of purpose, a new confidence in themselves and, above all, a new faith in Almighty God and in the blessings which have been waiting to be claimed by them.

Solitude in a Metropolitan City makes many people feel lonesome, isolated, neglected and all too often rejected. In the solitude of life in the country one can breathe the breath of Liberty and Freedom, one can vibrate to the vast expanse of Nature filled with every good thing that man should want. In such peaceful environment a person can FEEL God, can commune with God, finding rest, release, and consequent relaxation. Human lives are greater than all the brick and concrete structures of the City. In a Metropolitan City one cannot enjoy the wild flowers, the vast variety of birds, the joyful frolicsome denizens of the field and forest, the streams and running brooks.

The fields and woods provide a myriad assortment of EDIBLE wild plants, flowers, roots, berries in abundance for the nourishment of man and his family.

Of course there is the question of private property, and you would not want to trespass on other people's grounds, any more than you would want to have people trespass over your property.

Taking everything into consideration, what more can any man want? Just one thing: = A trip to look for HIS home IN THE COUNTRY, not too far from the sources of things he will need to buy from time to time, and LIVE WITH A PURPOSE.

2.
Would You call it a gamble?

Would you sit on the bank of a river
Waiting for it to be dried
So you could, with nary a shiver
Reach the bank on the other side?

Such folks do not Live, they just linger.
To make a move, they would dread.
They even won't move a finger
Beyond where they've settled their bed.

How many are ready to move
And experience a joyous Living?
Here's one who got out of his groove
For a life full of purpose and meaning.

N.W.W.

James was a young man in the Metropolitan City. He had just turned 34. Listen to what he has to say about leaving his City environment into which he was born, grew up and married. On his daily tredmill he was seeking an answer to LIVING LIFE with a PURPOSE.

I had been on my job 10 years, working for what? Money and promotion! I decided that I did not want to sacrifice my health for either one.

I quit my job a couple of years ago. I went home to find my wife, Joyce, weary and discouraged with life. Our two children, Jimmy, 9, and Linda, 7, at cross purposes. Now there I was, without a job.

"Honey," I said to my wife, "let's get ready to go for a drive tomorrow, out in the country somewhere. Pack so we can stay away 2 or 3 days if we decide to do so."

Instantly there was peace and anticipation in the apartment and the two children were jubilant.

Next morning we started out without any plans or itinerary. About 150 miles from home we came to a little town and stopped for lunch. Coming out of the restaurant I noticed a Real Estate Office next door. On a hunch I went in and told the Broker I would like to find a place in the country.

"I have just the place for you," he said. "Park your car here and we'll take my station wagon".

Five miles North of the town he stopped in the weed-smothered driveway of a small dilapidated little house, with some broken windows; two of the shutters were leaning on their side, each hanging from one hinge. There was not a speck of paint on the walls.

To us City-bred people the place looked utterly discouraging and impossible, but the Broker took us through the house, anyway. Step by step he showed us how we could fix the place up beautifully ourselves at little cost. Then he took us through a forest of weeds to the equally dilapidated chicken-coops and barn in the back and educated us in the art of fixing up old buildings.

How much land goes with the house? I asked. He told me 40 acres and the price was very reasonable. They were asking $10,000 but to settle the estate he thought they would be ready to deal with me.

Joyce and I went into a tongue-huddle. After all, I told her, rent money never paid interest. A home of our own is the only place for freedom and liberty. I asked the Broker if we could buy the house with about 10 acres, with an option for 5 years on the remaining 30 acres.

The Broker thought he could arrange that, and he did. We made a small down-payment out of our savings and closed the deal.

When I spoke to him about the discouraging condition of the weed-infested grounds, he amazed us by saying: "Why, that's the best indication that the soil is very fertile. You will have no trouble, no difficulty growing all your food on this soil".

The accompanying sketch will give you an idea of what the place looked like the following year.

What others have done, you, too, can do.

3.

your Opportunity

How beautiful, this Planet Earth
With all that mortal man can need.
Of opportunities there is no dearth,
Like flowers, they blossom from a seed.

How rich, this day and generation,
With opportunities on every hand
Waiting for your resignation
To return back to the land.

Land which our Fathers, with their sweat and tears
Recovered for Almighty God,
To live in Freedom, free from fears,
And cultivate this blessed sod.

Here is Your chance, my Reader Friend.
Bestir yourself while still there's time.
Everything in this life comes to an end.
End your confusion. Change to a better clime.

N.W.W.

This interesting World we live in today is still full of opportunities for pioneering, even though, to all appearances, all the available land has been taken up and is owned by someone.

There was never a more exciting time in which to live than in this day and generation. Daily I thank Almighty God for having created this BEAUTIFUL PLANET EARTH and all that is on it, and of having given me the opportunity to live on it long enough to see the tremendous developments which have taken place during my lifetime.

Today, if we live in the country, we do not have to undergo the many hardships which confronted our Ancestors who settled in this GREAT LAND. They were so busy establishing a home and grinding out a daily existence, that to just keep body and soul together was a monumental task, accomplished only by the strong and the brave.

As our GREAT LAND developed to the point where our Gross National Product made it possible for such a plentiful supply of goods and services to be available, that even the poor could afford them, people began to change. Parents who had been born and raised under an economic depression decided that they did not want their children to go through the many hardships they had undergone. Consequently one generation after another tried to give increasingly more of this World's material things to their children, until the present generation is in a state of genuine rebellion against "THINGS".

Study this younger generation and you will find that they are a most interesting progeny of young people, for the most part well educated but utterly lost in so far as material ambitions are concerned. They are seeking—seeking—trying to find something which has some real value in it, and when they do find their answer they begin to live a more purposeful life.

These young people study their parents, and the majority of that older generation, and the generation before that. They decide very definitely that they do not want to continue that chain in their generation because, generally speaking, their parents, and perhaps their grand-parents, never enjoyed any real happiness. Why, therefore, should they continue in their footsteps? These young people want to do some REAL WORTHWHILE LIVING, IF they can find a way of doing so.

The rebellion of these youngsters is open and unabashed, which is evident by their complete departure from everything so-called "orthodox",—in their clothing, their hair styles, their language and the kind of life they choose to live.

Almighty God established the correct pattern for the people of this Planet to follow. This is outlined in His instruction Book, THE HOLY BIBLE. He laid out in unequivocal language the blessings which should be anticipated and enjoyed, by those who chose to follow His instructions. Conversely, He enumerated the curses and the misery which could be expected to befall those who deliberately chose to go their own way and have nothing to do with His instructions.

I will confess that up to some 20 years ago both my wife and I thought we KNEW the Bible, both of us having an excellent religious background. However, when our attention was directed to a study of the 10 Commandments we were pulled up short, so to speak. When the 3rd chapter of the Book of Malachi (the last Book in the Old Testament) was emphatically pointed out to us, we really were jolted and shaken. This chapter has to do with God's 10% share of WHATEVER our income is. It is known as the Law of the TITHE. Go ahead and read this chapter and you will understand better what happened to us.

It was ordained thousands of years ago, to remain in full force and effect to this very day, that THE HOME was to be the basic foundation for God's people, with beautiful, healthy children to grace it. H E outlined the plan whereby the husband is to love and cherish his wife, and she is to love him and be a dutiful wife and a loving Mother. The husband is to take the responsibilities of supplying the home and whatever they need. The wife is to take care of the home and make it a comfortable place for them and for their children to live happily together. They are to share the responsibilities of teaching and training their children from His instruction book, the HOLY BIBLE, so that they may grow into healthy, strong, intelligent children. These, in turn, would grow up to find husbands and wives from similar families, and repeat the process. This Planet Earth could then be populated with strong, healthy, normal God-fearing individuals and grow into MIGHTY NATIONS.

At the summit and pinnacle of all the great Nations on this Planet Earth, Our GREAT UNITED STATES OF AMERICA stands supreme, in having been founded by our Ancestors who were searching for a land where they could be free to worship God as they wished, without having to follow any special kind of religion in which they could not believe, and which was dictated to them by another human being.

We have opened our doors to people from every land, who felt oppressed, and longed for FREEDOM. FREEDOM is so much a part of our basic fiber that it is something which everyone feels they would sacrifice anything to maintain. Our younger generation is trying to express this FREEDOM in every area of its life, today. BUT one cannot be FREE and live contrary to the Laws in God's instruction book for His people.

What makes life so interesting and vital today is that each person has equal opportunity in this GREAT LAND, to choose whatever he or she wishes to do.

On the surface, it would seem that one would find little difficulty in making the right choice, but it is not as easy as that. Education is readily available to all who wish to avail themselves of it, but there are so many things from which to make a choice, that one easily becomes confused. It is rather like going into an elaborate Smorgasbord to eat, with such a large variety of tempting, mouth-watering foods to choose from that one finds it difficult to make a choice. After all, the capacity of the stomach has a limit, and one could not possibly partake of even a small portion of everything displayed so attractively. The big question, then, is WHAT SHALL I CHOOSE, so that I can enjoy my meal to the utmost and still be comfortable and happy after eating. The choice creates a lot of confusion and indecision—which is an unhappy state of affairs. So it is with life. The same question arises,—what should I do and what would be the best for me and for my family?

As our GREAT LAND became more productive and our goods and services increased, so that we were no longer plagued with shortages, when there was enough for all to enjoy the fruits of our production and of their labor, more people began to move into Metropolitan Cities where they had dreamed for years that they would find and enjoy "a better life" and more cultural advantages for the children.

The unending chain of the fabulous discoveries and inventions of Modern Science brought more luxuries and so-called labor-saving devices into our home than we ever dreamed possible, and at prices which everyone could afford.

I can remember reading in a newspaper many, many years ago, about a man who had spent all the years of his vocational life in the Office of Patents of the United States of America, in Washington, D.C. The item published was the occasion of his having committed suicide. The reason he gave in a note which he left behind was that everything that could possibly be invented had now been invented, so there was nothing else for him to do but to step out—by means of suicide.

One would think that all the new contrivances we have today would bring happiness and contentment to our homes,—but has it? On the contrary. The very things which should have released us from so much of the drudgery of daily living, while giving us more time to do some of the things we had never been able to find time to do before, seem to have worked in reverse. We sometimes feel that we are "slaves to conventional modern living" from which there is no escape. What to do about it is the big question looming large before each one of us today.

4.
Country Life summons You

Let our unceasing, earnest prayer
Be for more light - for strength to bear
Our portion of the weight of care
That crushes into dumb despair
One half the human race in City's lair.

Oh suffering and sad humanity!
Oh ye afflicted ones who lie
Steeped to the ears in misery.
Patient, though sorely tried,
When the deep fountains of the heart
By strong convulsions rent apart
Are flowing all to meet an ebbing tide,
Yearning for freedom to the country-side.

N.W.W.

A famine anywhere does not keep the weeds from growing profusely where there is sufficient moisture. Thousands of weeds and plants growing wild are EDIBLE, food for humans, often more nutritious than the cultivated vegetables. Edible weeds and wild growing plants are found nearly everywhere in the country. They do not grow in Cities in concrete buildings, on cement sidewalks and asphalt pavements.

These weeds and wild growing plants generally have roots boring 30 to 50 feet down into the soil, where they collect moisture and trace elements which are not available near the surface of the ground.

What does the country have to offer? What advantages are gained by living on 5 or 10 acres or more when in close proximity to fields, pastures, woods, dirt roads and country lanes?

Apart from the food angle, consider H E A L T H as it is affected by the polluted atmosphere of the Metropolitan City and of general Metropolitan areas. Compare even the best aspects of a Metropolitan City to the pure air, general atmosphere and environment of fields and woods, of mountains, hills and running streams with their innumerable variety and quantity of EDIBLE wild vegetation.

Many of the weeds which the farmers abhor and detest, are NUTRITIOUS FOOD. They don't appreciate their nutritive ingredients. Weeds which they THINK are troublesome, may be actually nourishing and watering from underground streams the very crops they are planting. Vast numbers of people the world over quite naturally use these weeds and wild growing plants regularly as FOOD, as sustenance, as NOURISHMENT, throughout the year, through Spring, Summer and Fall, with plenty to keep them nourished through the Winter, at no cost.

WARNING = When foraging for edible weeds and wild plants, be sure you do not trespass on property owned by other people.

This plethora of EDIBLE wild plants is in addition to your growing your own vegetables, fruits and berries, food which you and your family have been accustomed to eat. Working your own garden is the very finest form of HEALTHY exercise you can have, and the most rewarding.

I suppose you wonder if you will get enough PROTEIN by eating vegetables and fruits? How much protein do you think you need, daily? If you eat much more than 4 to 6 ounces of concentrated protein a day you are overdoing it. Actually, TWO eggs can furnish all the concentrated good quality protein that is needed by an adult for his day's supply—provided the eggs are not "factory eggs". In order to be good nourishing eggs the hens that lay them must first of all have the freedom to roam around the garden or farm. Cooped up in cages the hens lose about 25% of the nutritional value of their eggs, mainly because they have not been mated with a rooster. Also because their cooped-up condition militates against the natural exercise and freedom, besides grubbing and scratching the ground as Nature intends they should.

The fertilizer which a flock of poultry provides is of great advantage as a component of your compost.

Poultry can also be of financial assistance to your budget. One dozen hens can lay from 200 to 250 DOZEN eggs a year. One rooster can take care of fertilizing a dozen hens and, with an automatic incubator, you could raise a prodigious crop of chickens a year.

If you have children you should keep a few Bantams. Their presence in the garden and field is always heart-warming. They are such an attractive sight to behold. The subject of poultry is covered in greater detail in a subsequent chapter.

If you keep a few GUINEA fowl you may not need to have any other kind of a watch-dog. Their presence on the farm will cause them to squawk "to beat the band" at the approach of a stranger, whether such be a human or a predatory animal or bird. Besides, Guinea eggs are considered by many as gourmet food. The next following chapter will undoubtedly be of interest to you. Be sure to study it.

Do not overlook the matter of HONEY. Two or three beehives may not seem much, or they may seem quite expensive to start with. But oh what an investment it is. The satisfaction of their producing your own honey, clean, not overheated nor diluted, year in, year out is certainly worth it.

Furthermore, you should have bees in order to pollinate your vegetables and fruits. This subject is also found in a subsequent chapter. Of course you already know you should NEVER use sugar. If an honest and informed Government took cognizance of the damage to the human system by the ingestion of sugar, sugar would be classed as a poison and its process and sale forbidden. USE HONEY for all your sweetening needs.

In so far as a regular daily supply of protein is concerned, nuts, seeds and sprouted seeds are very rich and excellent protein foods which must not be neglected.

5.
The City and the Boy

Whoever can guess the thoughts of a boy?
Like a magnet they cling to whatever is close.
Let a father and son, in the country, enjoy
Daily working together on the farm that they chose.

The boy will grow up imbued as with fire.
Perspective is shaped by his closeness to Dad.
His thoughts and ideals grow higher and higher-
That's a good program for every lad.

N.W.W.

In order to have a good foundation upon which to base a decision to move to the country from the Metropolitan City, one must first have the urge and the keen desire for country life. To move out to the country simply to get away from it all, without the deep incentive to put your shoulder to the wheel and create success by your efforts to cultivate the ground, and to do all the other chores required to keep and to maintain your dominion, would only generate greater frustration and dissatisfaction.

There is no question about it, a family with children is definitely handicapped in a very broad sense by living in a Metropolitan City. It is very rare that a father can have meaningful fellowship with his boys, when he has to leave the home in the early morning, and does not return until it is almost time for the young ones to go to bed. They do not have the opportunity to develop communication.

It is not surprising that boy after boy leaves home trying to fend for himself, because of not having had the daily contact with father which tends to give the boy balance.

In this connection, read the following dissertation on his boyhood days, exactly as Mr. Oscar E. Torkelson has expressed it under the heading:

"I HAD PAPA"

If you are fortunate enough to have children, and particularly boys, in your family, I need not add another word on this subject. Mr. Torkelson's lucid account should inspire every father so inclined, to start figuring how he and his family can attain a state of greater happiness, freedom and success by moving away from the restrictions of life in the Metropolitan City, into God's wide open country.

Mr. Torkelson's early training by his father on the farm established the foundation upon which he is today functioning as a well balanced adult, helping others, devoting his life to the ministry of counseling on the problems of marriage, of the family and of the child. He lives on Route No. 1, Gibsonia, Pennsylvania, Zip 15044. I am deeply indebted to Mr. Torkelson for his permission for me to include this dissertation in this book.

Thirteen of us sat in a circle in a personality-growth group.

Two hours each week we sat there, trying to get in touch with our inner feelings. Perhaps we could have been called an awareness group. Eventually a member would venture to expose himself, seeking help to put himself in focus. I was attending in order to satisfy one requirement of a course I was taking in school.

I noticed that it was painful for a member to talk about his life-long anger toward a parent. There were stern minutes when someone would reveal the hostility he felt toward his spouse. We grappled together to help a man discover his real feelings about his homosexual tendencies. One man had most of us in tears as he told about his fights with a physical problem. During one entire two-hour session none of us gave a glimpse of a smile as a man told the anguishing story of forcing himself to stay in the ministry; he had lived a 20-year lie.

One by one the real selves with their real problems surfaced. I began to feel that some of the members were wondering why I didn't confess my secret self. I saw glances that seemed to say, "We're looking for a way to get behind your veneer." Pressure kept building. "He'll have to break down pretty soon." Each member in a group like this has a personality, and the group itself has a personality. That's probably where the term *group dynamics* comes from. "We've got to know who you are," I kept hearing, and I could feel the hostility mounting.

But I had no problem. Oh, of course, I had problems, but no in-depth problem that I couldn't deal with myself. I felt that the group would think me a phony if I couldn't get in touch with my problems. I sympathized with the others in their problems, but I had nothing to parallel them. All the problems I could think of would sound so artificial, so feeble, so affected that if I did bring any of them before the group, I would be in a worse situation than if I didn't mention them.

Then one day I asked Tom how a professional problem he had disclosed much earlier had been resolved. He snapped back, "Do you want to help me, or do you want to know how the problem was resolved?"

"Well," I said, "I really didn't feel you were in need of support. I guess I'll have to admit I was inquiring how the problem was resolved." Twenty-four eyes swung round and focused on me.

The members of the group tried to get to what they thought was the real hostile person behind my smiling face. But I just couldn't find him, and told them so. Orville said, "What do you want from us, love?"

"Yes," I replied, "but not as a multiple, compound hug. Just your understanding and love."

Sylvia said, "Maybe you're not in touch with your feelings. Didn't your dad ever hug you?" She seemed eager to cinch my feellessness.

At that my story tumbled out.

I can't remember that my dad ever hugged me, but I felt his love, plenty of it. He was the first son born of my grandparents after they emigrated from Norway. He had been schooled in the philosophy that the husband is the head of his house. No one questioned Father. My two older brothers learned to keep their distance from him. They solved their own problems and retained their own feelings. Seven years later when I was born my dad did an about-face.

He didn't want the isolation he had built around himself. He set about in an honest way to be a real companion to me, and he succeeded.

When I was five or six, I was helping Papa (we called him Papa until we were fully grown) pile some scrap lumber by the barn on our 60-acre farm in eastern Kansas. I got a splinter in my hand and it hurt. I didn't dare let him see me cry. At the first opportunity, I started for the house to have Mamma take the splinter out.

Papa saw that I was in pain, and he probably saw my shame and embarrassment. I expected him to scold me for being so clumsy. Instead he kindly asked me to let him look at my hand. Then he told me he thought he could remove the splinter with the small blade of his pocket knife. Tenderly he held my small soft hand in his large calloused one. Gently he worked while he asked if it was hurting too much. He got the splinter out. "Bet it hurt; it was in pretty deep," he sympathized. After that I recall nothing but deep trust in Papa.

I followed him wherever I could. There were sisters to do the housework with Mamma indoors. My older brothers were big enough to help their uncles. I was Papa's helper. My life revolved around Papa and Papa's farm.

Papa seemed to be in touch with the whole out-of-doors. He could predict a blizzard by the way the telephone wires sang. He propped up an old hollow post one spring so a bluebird could nest in it one more season. He was aware when the bees were ready to swarm, and he would have a hive built for the occasion. He seemed to know when a hen was hiding her nest. He could tell when the cows would soon push down a fence to reach the growing corn.

He talked about the geese flying south. He explained the dangers of the flooded creek. He revealed his fear of the devastating invading grasshoppers. He explained the 17-year locust. I crawled to the top branches to pick apples while Papa picked fast from the ground. I picked up the potatoes while he plowed them out.

On winter evenings from the time I was only eight or nine we milked in the barn warmed by the heat of the cows and lighted by a kerosene lantern. That was always the highlight of a day. From the zinging ping of the stream of milk hitting the bottom of an empty pail to the mellow music of a stream foaming a half-full pail, we talked. We talked about school, about cows having calves, about honesty, about religion, about health. Sometimes we would squirt a stream of milk into a cat's open mouth, and we'd laugh at the ridiculous fielding. Sometimes the milking sounds stopped, and we caught ourselves in that dim light just talking, but the sound of the cows munching hay went on.

I don't know why Papa wanted me to go to the timber to help cut the winter's supply of stove wood; surely he could have done it quicker by himself. I could hardly hold onto my end of the six-foot crosscut saw, but I did. I had my ax, and I was taught how to help keep it sharp by not hitting the dirt. I was expected to oil the saw so it wouldn't get rusty. I had to herd the cows on a deserted road during the summers' drought. I gathered the eggs and watered the mules. It was fun. Papa needed my help. He showed me how to cut corners; he complimented me when I did a job well and quickly.

Papa liked good times—not excitement. We had the uncles and cousins in for watermelon. The melons were cold from being in the cellar. We had picnics with roasting ears and peach cobbler. Papa always kept one safe swing in a high branch; he checked it from time to time with a tall extension ladder. Papa had screw-on racing skates when the ponds froze. He helped us kids with strap-on skates. He couldn't afford to buy new ones for us, but he would pick up old ones at some auction. Papa helped us keep our sleds painted and repaired. Papa helped us with the wooden-rimmed bicycle. How I loved to hear Papa laugh. How I dreaded his look of disapproval!

As I grew older, I was left with more and more of the work and chores around the farm. Papa worked for the neighbors hanging paper, painting, doing repair work. He depended on me more and more, and I liked to please him. He didn't kiss me or hug me. I knew how he felt by his squints and glances and winks and laughs and grunts and silences. There was no question about how we were getting along with each other; we never attempted to hide our feelings, and we had plenty in common to feel about.

Then when I was about 17 I decided to go away to a boarding school. My, I was homesick! I thought of Papa milking alone. I thought of Papa getting in wood alone. I thought of Papa shucking corn alone. I longed for the little farm— the security and happiness of relaxed, meaningful living. I was brought up on love and trust. I don't believe it's in me to hate or to hold old grudges. I like living this way.

The 12 pairs of eyes in the group that focused on me were friendly eyes now. No one was interrupting me or challenging me. I did not feel misunderstood. I was not phony—not even to those 12 members. Best of all, I knew I was genuine! I had felt the goodness of Papa and what that goodness and bigness had meant to me as I was growing up. I had no real need to be in the group. I had no problem; I had had Papa.

6.
Be a Doer—not a Wishful Thinker

If thou art worn and hard beset
With sorrows that thou wouldst forget,
If thou wouldst read a lesson that will keep
Thy heart from fainting and thy soul from sleep,
Go to the woods and hills!—No tears
Dim the sweet look that Nature wears.

Longfellow

From the cool vastness of the midnight air
My spirit drank such sweet repose
To be refreshed when mornings bear
The exotic perfume of a fragrant rose.

N.W.W.

What a strange paradox—We become burdened, weary and nervous over our occupation and environment in the Metropolitan City, yet habit has made such an incursion into our consciousness that it seems as if only a supernatural force could move us out of our groove.

How often, what we vow we would never do, is exactly what we end up doing, then realize it is the best thing we ever did. Did you ever experience that? Did you ever discover that never does a door close but that a better one does not open?

You may say that you LOVE the Metropolitan City, that you could never settle for a place in the country, that you want neighbors and the activities that surround you in the large City. You want constant human contact. Perhaps that is where you belong. Or perhaps maybe you have never lived in the country. Maybe you were born in the country and deserted it when too young to know any better?

Do you know what the polluted atmosphere of the Metropolitan City and Suburbs does to a person's lungs? If you have ever studied the lungs of a Metropolitan City dweller, you will understand why so many such City people fail to live to enjoy healthy and happy sunset years of life, and find life, based on scores of years of experience, as an interesting and productive period of longevity. This should be the best time of our life.

It is the person with foresight who is considered lucky, when events leave a trail of wishful thinkers behind. Achievement and success can be the result of thoughtful planning at any age.

Metropolitan City life does have many advantages, of that there is neither question nor doubt. However, is it the N O W that counts,—or is it the unforeseeable future? Health, energy, vigor, vitality, liberty and freedom are not attained immediately—on demand. There is no comparison between these attributes of Health which were intended from the very beginning of things for man to enjoy, by living in the country, and the circumscribed environment of Metropolitan City living.

The Garden of Eden was created by Almighty God as a pattern, as an example for the myriad generations to follow, but man was expelled from the Garden of Eden because he disobeyed God's instructions. (Genesis 3: 17)

We cannot live without food. One cannot grow all one's food in a Metropolitan City, under normal circumstances. One is therefore dependent on others, on food stores and markets, on transportation and not the least, on farmers and gardeners who grow the food—IN THE COUNTRY.

Individual families with a home in the country and a few acres to boot, can use the Law of Prevention and Survival. They can grow most of their own food. Not so with the Metropolitan City folks. Metropolitan City folks are entirely dependent on supply and demand, and the consequent and unpredictable state of the Economy.

Furthermore, there is the serious problem of the population explosion. This is resulting in vast lands throughout the country being converted from food production to community housing and industrial developments. Your 5 or 10 acres or more, in a well chosen location can safeguard you from encroachment and secure your future Economy. This can supply you and your family with the means of self-preservation and perhaps even SURVIVAL.

If your little farm is close and handy to a town or small City, you may have ample opportunity to dispose of your surplus food, which would be of a quality not often available in the local markets.

When you grow food of better quality than that obtainable locally, you may have more demand for what you grow than you can supply. This has proved inevitable.

Furthermore, such a project would be a benefit to the families who do not grow their own food and who are interested enough to come to you for your surplus food. You would be doing them a favor, besides providing yourself with an income.

What a coincidence! Just as I finished re-typing this chapter in this manuscript, the Postman brought my mail and the first letter I saw was from my Friend Mr. Henry Marshall, whose acquaintance you will make in a subsequent chapter in this book. You will be interested in these few lines: =

"You know, most of us are so confined and pinned down by urban life—and import it via TV and newspapers—in day to day living—it is only on occasion—as recently, when I flew to Florida from Los Angeles and back, then drove from California to Wisconsin, that you realize how MUCH beautiful, un-touched, unspoiled land there still is—thank God!"

7.
Did a famine ever afflict You?

Who ever failed to love the calm and quiet moods
  Of fleeting clouds o'er hill and dale,
Of bubbling brook amid the tangled woods
  Meandering through the moss-grown shale?
Blue skies, the silver clouds, and no discordant din.
  Groves through whose broken roof the sun looks in.
The flowers, the leaves, the hedgerow 'round the field.
  The pastel hues that stain the wild bird's feather
And flush the clouds which yield and yield
  Through April's breezes, sun and rain together
To change its costume to the blue of May
  With fragrant roses and with new-mown hay.

N.W.W.

Older people can well remember National financial depressions. Young folks live in the illusory state of self-deception that leads them to the conclusion that if everything is going along well now, it has always done so and will continue to do so. Because they are accustomed to reach for the telephone to span miles of distances to talk to others, it has always been so.

Because they can have light and heat at the flip of the finger, that everybody since the days of Noah has done the same.

Amazing, isn't it? Were WE the same, at their age? What and how much have we learned in the meantime?

We who have the years of experience upon which to base our opinions know perfectly well that disasters follow in cycles and depressions are National disasters.

To face reality, we look into the future, and while we cannot predict our destiny, we can calculate the problems of PREVENTION, which is nothing more nor less than prudence, discretion and foresight.

Age can take advantage of the experiences of the past, and if we do so, we call it hindsight. Oh for the gift to use our hindsight with which to project our foresight, that our foresight might be benefited by our hindsight.

Older folks can recall the distressing conditions which prevailed in depressions. Those who are wise, either have already made provision for future economic security or are busy doing so now.

Will the younger generation, in this respect, follow in the steps of the older generations? Many are doing so. Yes, many have already done so. How many of the vast innumerable horde can be awakened to the needs of the future? How many can be uncoupled, disentangled and alienated from the illuding spectre of philosophical speculative phenomena which has so entranced the ill-informed? Time only will tell. Meanwhile Hearts will be broken and will continue to be broken because the progeny has wandered so far away from reality into the realm of phantasmagoria. It doesn't pay, but young people must learn their lessons the hard way. It has always been thus and I suppose it will ever so be.

Meanwhile there, beyond the Metropolitan City's limits lies the vast field of future experience, physical, mental and spiritual growth.

Plants grow today as they did thousands of years ago, since the creation of vegetation on this Earth. In the beginning, as in the present day and generation, such vegetation was created for the use and benefit of man, for his nourishment and SURVIVAL, for his

PRESERVATION, and for the benefit of his posterity. Hence the stupenduous, inordinate, unlimited supply of EDIBLE plants and weeds growing WILD in so many areas of this good Earth.

8.
Something to think about

My spirit, like the transparent air
*   That clothes the hillsides from above,*
Though not of earth, encloses there
*   A memory with thoughts of love.*

In the night, in the City's stillness,
*   I have watched the hours glide*
Till the fear of starving illness
*   Overflowed me like a tide.*

Now, alas, my soul remembers
*   Chances I once had to start*
Life anew—like living embers,
*   On a farm, to fire my heart.*

Now the shadowy country I see
*   In my dreams = a fruitful land*
With abundant food for me
*   And some to spare on every hand!*

N.W.W.

Documentation: the KANSAS CITY TIMES, August 29, 1974.

The food shortage of 1974 is pointing us back to the Bible. We have read in Genesis that "God said, Let the earth bring forth grass, the herb yielding seed. . . God

saw that it was good . . . to you it shall be for meat"
(Genesis 1:11, 12, 29.)

Because of a widespread famine in the world of 1974 man is being forced to consider for food what he has neglected for centuries. In particular, Americans who are the best fed people on the face of the earth, are being compelled to reconsider what God wrote for the human race—"grass . . . it shall be for meat". An article from the Kansas City Times, August 29, 1974 emphasizes this: Here is the quote:

SCIENTISTS SEEKING FOOD AMONG GRASS AND LEAVES (Service of the Washington Star-News)- Washington—Carrot tops, pea vines, bean leaves and lake weeds are not ordinarily considered gourmet fare, but in the face of rising food prices, crop failures and chronic hunger in the underdeveloped world, a growing number of scientists are taking another look at the heretofore neglected potential of the 'inedible' parts of Plants. 'Of the 20 amino acids from which proteins are built, 8 must be supplied to man from the leaves of green plants', said Mark A. Stahlmann, a biochemist. 'These so-called 'essential' amino acids are produced in green leaves through photosynthesis and then only part are concentrated into seeds, tubers and animal products which will be consumed by man. The conversion of leaf protein into seed protein is wasteful. Only 8 to 20% of the protein fed to farm animals is recovered as protein for human nutrition. Over 21 million tons of vegetable wastes containing 393,000 tons of protein are lost yearly in the United States alone'. Currently one of a team of scientists and engineers working on leaf protein at the University of Wisconsin, Stahlmann first became aware of its possibilities while in England in 1961. At that time he learned that the British, during World War II, had developed a machine similar to a hammer mill that would separate protein from fiber in leaves, squeezing out a digestible juice". [End of quote.]

This enterprising American scientist returned to America and set out to obtain vegetable tops, potato and pea vines, aquatic plants from lakes, and reduced these to pulp and removed the fibers. He discovered with his colleagues that these materials contained as much or nearly as much good quality protein as cow's milk or hens' eggs. Like milk nearly all the essential amino acids were discovered in generous quantities. We can easily recognize from these stored foods God has made available to each generation of man from Adam, that God graciously provided food for us in most unlikely places. Since our public schools are no longer permitted to use the Bible, it will be increasingly difficult for us to heed Solomon's advice: "Remember now thy Creator in the days of thy youth. . ." (Eccl. 12:1) Grass and leaf eating may be one reminder to our generation of neglecting our Bibles. Thanksgiving month should remind us that we should not forget to thank God for grass and seed He intended for us to eat for our essential nourishment, and the bread of life.

(Note:: This entire chapter has been copied from Dr. David Webber's publication Volume 1 Number 9 "Bible in the News"-Except the poem.)

9.
When is it too early to start?

No, nothing ever drops out of the blue
  By accident. There's always a design.
In every phase of life, for me and You,
  The answer, when worked out, becomes benign.

No door does ever close than one much better
  Will open. That's the Plan for those who're wise,
Who are ready and prepared to loose their fetter
  And grasp their obvious chances when they arise.

Bestir yourself, my Friend. Let others worry
  Over their luck—or lack of luck—in life.
A glorious future—Freedom—without hurry
  Is waiting in the Country, for you and your wife.

N.W.W.

"When I was fourteen my father gave me an acre of land. "Make and save all you can," he said. "You must learn how to make a dollar."

"I planted tomatoes, a new wilt resistant variety developed by Dr. Norton of the Maryland Agricultural Experiment Station. My neighbors liked the new variety. "Will you sell us seed?" they asked. I did, and started in the seed business.

"Growing tomato seed paid my way through the University of Maryland Agricultural College. As orders began to come in from distant States I started to print a catalog. Yes, all this business grew out of a single package of tomato seed."

The foregoing appeared in Mr. Otis S. Twiller's Seed catalog which I received a while back.

How true it is that from little acorns huge magnificent Oak trees grow. If the acorn knew enough to be afraid of failure, we would have no Oak trees.

I am sure that half of the things that people fail to succeed in are the result of their fear to take the first step, their fear to make the attempt.

Everybody wants freedom. Everybody wants to be free from their present work when it is not compatible with their temperament and ambitions. Everybody wants to be free from their environment when they feel fenced in or with incompatible neighbors.

Where is such freedom? We find it in a complete change of work and of environment—out in God's country, out, growing one's own food, out, where independence is the fruit of one's own efforts and ingenuity for those who are so inclined.

A century ago City life was totally different from what it is today. . Looking back at an article which appeared in the Scientific American magazine in July 1899, when the automobile was yet in its infancy and Henry Ford had not yet made his first Model which became a reality about 12 or 14 years later, some nostalgic prophecies were made. Optimistically, it was foreseen that the "horseless carriage" or "motor car" would be most beneficial in the future, particularly to people living in the Cities. The concept at the time was that in the future the light, rubber covered tires on automobiles, in contrast to the steel rimmed wheels on horse drawn vehicles, would provide swiftly moving conveyances traveling noiselessly over streets that would be clean, odorless and dustless, with particular emphasis on the relief from nervousness, distraction and strain "of modern (1899) Metropolitan City life". What a contrast that picture is, to our late 20th century Metropolitan City conditions!

I can remember as clearly as if it had happened only yesterday, when I was a little lad, probably not even 10 years old. My brother and I had covetously seen and carefully examined a beautiful 4-wheeled buggy, it was painted a vivid red, in the yard of a livery stable not far from where we lived. One day I went up to the owner of the stable—I can see him now, chewing on a fat cigar in his office above the stable—and asked him how much he would sell me that red buggy for. "Oh, he said, just bring me a nice beefsteak and you can have it". I immediately ran home and, taking a large sharp kitchen knife, I went into the larder and cut a hunk off a large piece of meat that was on the bottom shelf of the "cooler" (I could not have reached the higher shelves without bringing a chair and standing on it!). I wrapped the hunk carefully and took it to him. He said "That's fine, go help yourself". So my brother and I got between the shafts of the buggy and between us we started out of the yard for our garden. We had to pass a bakery shop on our way home and when we came abreast of it, the baker came running out and shouted at us "Hey, boys, where are you going with my buggy?" We told him in detail all about our purchase of it from the owner of the livery stable. He laughed and said we'd better leave the buggy right there and run along home, which we did before father might see us. Were THOSE REALLY the "good old days"?—I wonder?

10.
What others do, You can do, too.

I hear you calling me
From way beyond the maddening crowds.
I feel the urge to see thee,
Farm and Field, bathed in the dew of silvery clouds.
To hear the Lark gone wild to welcome me
Singing that wistful song that she projects.
Woodpeckers jubilantly drilling in the tree,
The Starling clasps his tiny castanets.

Why dream such details with precision?
Waste no more time, my boy, my lass,
  but make your own decision!

N.W.W.

Just as I concluded typing the preceding chapter and went into our dining room to eat a delicious dinner of organically grown vegetables in my salad, I received information about a family who lived in a New Jersey City of about 50,000 population. They bought a farm a few years ago and are living on it happily and successfully.

I am not at liberty to identify them, but for our purpose we will call them the John Smith family.

John is the Superintendent of a factory in that City. For many years the family had dreamed and yearned for a home in the country. John used to say the City is not the most favorable place to rear six children, particularly as his boys wanted to go in for agriculture.

A Real Estate Agent took them out to see a 30 acre farm in the country, a comparatively short distance from the City. It was near enough so that John could commute to his work. So they bought it.

The farm had a home on it, suitable for his family. It also had a barn and some poultry houses. It was just the place they had dreamed about. A place where they could grow their own vegetables and fruits, and facilities enough for poultry to supply them with eggs for their own need, and a plentiful surplus to sell.

It did not take the family long to get settled and accustomed to their allotted chores. Soon John decided to change the breed of his poultry to New Jersey Giants figuring that the heavier birds, with their larger egg production, both in size and quality and in yearly production, would be more profitable.

One day John took two one-dozen boxes of eggs to the shop and gave them to two of his men. The next day they enthusiastically ordered two dozen eggs each, to be delivered weekly, declaring they could not get such exceptionally good eggs in the market. That really set the family up in business. From a meager beginning of two dozen eggs, other factory and office workers created such a demand that their "fresh country eggs" business blossomed into weekly deliveries of scores of boxes directly to the Company's employees.

As the news spread, about the size and quality of their products, route deliveries were needed two days a week. Their prices are based on market quotations for Grade AA eggs.

"Because we are selling at retail prices, says John, we are able to be as successful as we are. Our quality defies competition."

John has no plans to expand beyond his family's ability to take care of the business. "Getting too big, he says, only brings more problems. We know that we can absorb some of our inefficiencies by higher prices, but even more important, where could you find a more wholesome atmosphere to bring up a daughter and five boys. We wouldn't go back to the City for worlds!"

The two older boys are students of Agriculture at the local College, the daughter and two of the boys are in High School and the youngest boy is in Grade school.

All of them get up early and help with the chores and with the jobs assigned to them. They also have chores to do when they get home from school in the afternoon.

They keep their place in "apple-pie" order, but admit that their most difficult problem is cleaning up and getting ready for a new lot of chicks and pullets.

However, they have their period of fun and exultation, too. Last year Jim had the reserve champion 4-H Club steer in the County Show and Bob had the Grand Champion capons in the County 4-H Round-up. Elaine is quite active with her 4-H sewing project which won for her a trip to the College 4-H Congress last Summer.

It seems quite apparent that Mr. and Mrs. John Smith have found a happy solution to that old problem of "how to keep them down on the farm".

11.
You prefer to live in the City?

Please imagine a space craft here from the stars.
A Martian walks out of it, a man from Mars.
Looking around in amazement, distressed,
Trying to find words, his shock he expressed.

This, he says, is not what we expected.
Planet Earth does not seem to have God much respected.

Where is the wonderful Garden of Eden
Where never was wanting food to be eaten,
Where every family on this Earth would be
Using honey and milk, under olive and fig tree?

What are those ugly patches with deep grooves and high
  With towers like ant hills built towards the sky
And those tiny insects chasing each other
  In a thick atmosphere enough people to smother,
Moving in lines at such senseless speed?
  Tell me, Mr. Earthman, what is their need?

Speak fast, Mr. Earthman, I cannot stay longer,
  The stench from these canyons reaches up yonder.

Those dreadful places are Cities, my Friend.
  Gregarious people live there. That's the trend.
The people down here are now close to Hell's borders,
  But God's Blessings are ever for who follow His Orders.
It's nice to have met you, great man from Mars.
  Maybe some day we'll come to the stars.

We've already been playing with expensive rockets
To shoot people to Mars locked up in sockets.

N.W.W.

It occurs to me that I seem to have done my best to induce everybody who lives in a Metropolitan City to pack up as quickly as possible, and flee to the country.

Suppose I tone that down somewhat and consider some incontrovertible facts.

In every community there has always been a settlement needed where produce and other merchandise, goods and commodities had to be available within certain circumscribed areas for more or less easy access and availability.

In the Far East such settlements grew into Bazaars. As communities became more extended congregations of humanity, stores began to appear and grew both in size and in importance.

In this day and generation, when Industry has become the core of civilized activity and existence, stores have ballooned into what are now our

Supermarkets and into assemblages of merchants known as Shopping Centers.

Without such Shopping Centers to which City people have become accustomed, those whose livelihood and very existence depends on their City living environment would be faced with the insurmountable problem of obtaining all their civilized living requirements.

On the other hand, the very presence of these thousands upon thousands of Metropolitan City dwellers makes it necessary for the merchants themselves to have their places of business conveniently accessible for the community.

If you prefer to live in the City, that's your privilege. I quite agree with you that thousands of people will have to continue to live in Metropolitan environments. Nevertheless, every Metropolitan community is harboring thousands of men and women who usually have a family for which they have to provide. Their very existence seems to be hanging on a very thin thread of uncertainty, if not of dissatisfaction and frustration. It is both surprising and amazing how many of these could move to a few acres in the country and begin a completely new life based on the Earth as the matrix of their success, with the rewards for their labors far surpassing the tenuous outlook of expectation, of well-being and of prosperity in a Metropolitan City against competition over which they have no control.

Do not let us overlook the children. As the twig is bent, so does the tree grow. The formative years of a child's life establish the pattern of the kind and type of man or woman it will be at maturity.

The child in a Metropolitan City is confined to the circumscribed experiences gathered from instruction and example to which it is exposed. Book learning, pictures, television and radio, of doubtful value, with perhaps strolls through the parks or occasional trips to the country. Are these a substantial foundation for learning what life is all about? No, indeed. These are superficial contacts with virtually no actual experience to grow upon.

And what about the father of the family? Does the child have any idea how father spends his time, what he does, what his responsibilities are? No, not the vaguest idea.

What does the child have to gain by living on at least a few country acres? It has EVERYTHING to gain that will awaken and alert the child in a comparatively short time to the activities in which the family is involved; with the right and the opportunity to participate in such activities and to learn from Mother Nature the basic living lessons which are incomprehensible to the Metropolitan City child. In the country, the child knows most of the time where father is, what he is doing or has to do, and all too often is able to participate in father's work and be helpful.

The child in the Metropolitan City rarely KNOWS its father. Father usually comes home fatigued from his daily activities which are a mystery to the child, and there is rarely any communication between them.

The father and child on the farm, on the other hand, have much in common, they can discuss matters and problems, they can communicate. The child can begin to formulate plans for its own future, usually not afraid to discuss anything with its parents.

These are matters which every family should consider very carefully when the question arises, to choose between City life and life on a few acres in the country.

The financial problem of moving from the City may be an important stumbling block. You may not be aware of the fact that there is a neighborly system, the Church-sponsored Credit Unions which have become widespread throughout the country among American Christians. There are more than 1350 religious units ranging from local parishes to whole denominations which now operate credit unions on a non-profit basis to help each other and themselves financially.

The country's largest credit union under church auspices is the Mt. Carmel credit Union in Pueblo, Colorado, with a membership of some 16,000 and assets of more than $18 million.

The American Baptist credit union in Covina, California, has more than 8,000 members and over $12 million in assets. The manager of the Central Texas Baptist credit union explained that these unions provide a way for people to bank together and help themselves. Most of the 23,000 credit unions in America are not operated by religious institutions. The basis of the credit unions in religious groups is mutual help and cooperation.

The Arizona Republic newspaper of August 23, 1975 gives an analytical account of these unions. It gives the instance of the Antioch Baptist church in Pontiac, Michigan, which started its credit union when many of its congregation were turned down by banks in emergencies. The church's pastor said: "Even the finance companies turned them down, and the church credit union has had only one default, in 4 years."

I gave you this information so that you may do your own investigation of the subject in the area where you plan to start your farm project.

Whatever the financial circumstances may be of these millions of people, there is no overlooking the fact, if they continue to live in the City, they have rent to pay, they must have means of getting to and from their work or occupation, they have to spend money for food, clothing and other necessities essential for City living.

If they were living in the country with their few

acres, a garden, some chickens and such, most of the expenses necessary for City living would be non-existent.

There are many ways and means to obtain a few acres in the country, if the will and ingenuity of the seeker are alive and alert to the situation. There are millions of acres throughout the United States which are not presently being constructively used. If the seeker can establish a standard of honesty, integrity and the will to succeed, he will find many openings awaiting only the knocking at the door. Realtors and Real Estate Brokers are always ready and anxious to make a deal where they and the seller can be financially satisfied, and the buyer can be contented with the transaction.

With all this understanding, let those who do not wish to live in the country continue to live in the City.

You who are ready for a change in your life and your fortunes, study this book carefully, page by page. Also study real estate and farm agency catalogues. Don't be discouraged if the place you think would suit your purposes seems too expensive or difficult to find. Of this you can be sure: Your place has been allotted to you, somewhere, and is waiting for you. Just exercise your patience.

The main thing is to get started, then go on from there. In my opinion, and judging from my experience, you can't lose anything by seeking, while on the other hand you may gain more than you ever imagined.

12.
The City and the Man.

After a day's work in the City at the office, at the store, at the shop, what next?

Does a man go "home" to his apartment expecting to find a welcoming, happy wife and 2 or 3 joyous children glad to see Daddy home? How often does that happen in a Metropolitan City?

I have lived in New York City and in other Megalopolies and have seen and observed the tired, anxious, and sometimes fearful demeanor of a Pater Familias (the father of the family) of a small, and sometimes not so small, family, as he returns from his day's efforts to keep family, body and soul in a living condition. This has been a lifetime burden to me, to see so much depression.

Shortly after this man enters his apartment, the reverberations of discord, of dissension, which has been brewing within the breast of his frustrated wife, begin to percolate through the windows and doors, and even through the walls of the apartment.

"Billy, I told you to pick up your toys, hurry up and do so right now! Hilda, I told you to wash yourself and get dressed before Daddy came home—now you'll have to wait till he gets through with the bathroom." Then a scream from little Judy: "Mommy, Billy is taking my dolly and won't let me play with his drums."

Poor Mommy! Does she get the sympathy and consideration she deserves after a frustrating day of trying to keep the apartment clean and in order, washing the children's clothes, getting an early breakfast for a grumpy husband and for 3 unruly children? Then lunch, after a fashion, for four, and finally trying to get together a dinner that she hopes will satisfy her breadwinner?

Unhappily, Daddy is in no mood to become the arbiter of disputes between 3 lively children. The dinner is very good, and the wife's wishful thinking that maybe he will be compatible, at least, and perhaps communicative, is shattered when she asks him what his plans, if any, are for the evening.

This is the moment he dreaded. Under his skin, deep in his heart, he really loves his family and does appreciate his wife. He wishes that he could make their apartment a real and happy home, but his super-sensitive ego forbids any display of such feelings. He feels inadequate, he feels he is a failure and that everybody knows it and condemns him, so he merely tells her he is going out "with the boys" for the evening.

At last, dinner is finished. What happens before he leaves has been splendidly portrayed by Mr. Henry Marshall in better words than I could muster. Mr. Marshall has a remarkable keen insight into the mind and thoughts of such a man as this Daddy. He wrote the following article which appeared in the August 1975 issue of the SIGNS OF THE TIMES Magazine, and which he has kindly consented to let me use as the core of this chapter. The article is entitled::

"DADDY, PLEASE
DON'T GET DRUNK!"

"Daddy, PLEASE don't get drunk tonight."

The small voice was pleading, fearful, desperate.

I looked down at her—the child of my heart, my dearest treasure. So little. So innocent. And so frightened. Frightened of me—her loving, adoring father—of what I would become if I drank. I had put this panic into those sweet eyes—into this pure being.

I DID want to get drunk tonight. I intended to. I was going to a party where everyone would drink, where there would be laughter and hilarity and escape. I could forget that my life was empty, futile, grim. I could forget the job I despised, the people I disliked. I could forget that I was a nonentity, overlooked, underappreciated, unfulfilled. I could forget that I was spiritually alone, adrift, alienated, with no sail or rudder, no anchor, no faith. I could forget that I was at war in a bitter, deadly, daily struggle with the woman I had promised to love, that we were a tormented, agonized, distraught family—the five of us.

GETTING DRUNK WAS FUN! Alcohol turned me on. I became witty, clever, ingenious, articulate, entertaining—instead of dull, stodgy, unnoticed, left out, as I usually was. People laughed. I had recognition, applause, status. I was SOMEBODY, I liked that.

Getting drunk was fun. Being drunk wasn't. Clumsy, foolish, babbling, incoherent, stupid, silly, sick, nauseated, dependent. Bereft of wit, charm, dignity, self-control—almost of humanity.

And that she should see me so—my darling child. And not know why. What did she know of my frustrations, fears, anxieties? What could she know of being hypersensitive in a brutal world, of being a misfit, of maladjustment, of emotional lacerations, of bleeding to death internally? What could she know of things that make people drink—people like me? Of why they can be willing to become swinish, brutish, loutish fools, hulks, derelicts?

"Daddy, PLEASE don't get drunk tonight." What could she know of what happens to drunks? Of what might happen to me? Do drunks get arrested, go to jail, get their pictures in the paper? Does everyone find out about them? Do they get in accidents, get killed, or kill others? Lose their jobs? Go to institutions? Die? Get divorced? Leave their families? Go broke? Hurt people? Even wives? Children? How could she know? How could she comprehend why a gentle, loving father would become a stranger, an idiot, a lunatic?

"Daddy, PLEASE don't get drunk tonight."
What agonies had I inflicted on this angelic
creature? Would she lie awake tonight, clutching
her doll, wondering, apprehensive, chilled with
fear that I might come home stumbling, bumbl-
ing, sick, stinking? Would she dream ghastly
dreams, her little head full of fiends, monsters,
fearful shapes and shadows, horrid shrieks and
sounds, dark and terrible fantasies? Could Satan
and all his imps and demons do greater torture
to my child?

"Daddy, PLEASE don't get drunk tonight."
Would this pathetic plea do for me what my
own self-disgust and remorse had not? Would
my will and resolve be hardened? Or would my
need to escape reality prevail, even at this awful
price, this incredible cruelty? Will a man do
ANYTHING to shed, however briefly, his woe,
the ache in his heart and in his stomach, his
weariness with life, his anonymity? Is no calamity
too great compared to the joy of forgetfulness,
oblivion, euphoria—and the transforming of oneself into a witless, puling, puking, puerile,
addled clod? Hating yourself and your weakness
is not enough. Is loving your child?

"Daddy, PLEASE don't get drunk tonight."
Could I reject that piteous entreaty? Could
YOU, Mr. Alcoholic?

(So wrote my Esteemed Friend, Mr. Henry
Marshall, 150 Kenney Street, Green Bay, Wisconsin,
54301.)

Now let us consider the other side of the coin. Let us
transfer "Daddy" and his family to a few acres way out
in the country, out from the imprisonment of a City
apartment. Let us see them all installed in the liberty
and freedom of open land in which to roam at will.
Daddy, no longer the frustrated, unwanted misfit, now
has his garden in which to grow all the vegetables and
fruits, organically, that his now happy family will
need. Bantam chickens for the children to play with

and care for. A flock of fine poultry, a flower garden and an herb garden for Mommy. Pygmy goats and Dexter young cattle, no less than beehives, for the whole family to be busy with and to enjoy.

Here meals are happy occasions. Here, under the canopy of a deep blue sky and surrounded by God's bounty, Daddy does not any more feel that destiny is closing in on him, does not any more feel the urge to "get away, with the boys". His labors are both interesting and constructive. He IS somebody, now. He owns the land—a part of his Great United States of America. His children are growing in intelligence and developing self assurance because they are now an integral part of the constructive work in which the whole family is involved. They are, and they feel that they are, a real help to Daddy and Mommy.

And Mommy herself is at last tasting the spiritual nectar that she dreamed of when their Honeymoon began.

In the Metropolitan City the family had the tendency to become overburdened by the closeness of its imprisonment in the apartment. In the country a life of happiness, success and achievement is possible by the opportunities for each to cooperate in the building up of the kind of family Almighty God intended for us to have.

Do not for one moment think that the foregoing example of the "Daddy" in Mr. Marshall's delineation of the mental involvement of a frustrated man depicts the only snare and delusion of Metropolitan City living. Not by a long way.

I need only refer very briefly to the thousands upon thousands—in fact millions of "up-and-coming" young (and not so young) Executives who indulge in so-called "innocent" cocktails several times a day. I wonder what these men would do if they realized that they are embarking on the most certain and dependable route to develop brain trouble, loss of memory, even fatal liver ailments and heart attacks within the brief period of 20 to 30 years of "just a few cocktails, Martinis"—or what have you in the alcohol line—just a few times daily?

One is not necessarily a drunkard or an alcoholic if one takes a few "sociable" drinks daily. However, the daily erosion invariably has its effect manifested usually in 20 to 30 years. Of what value is the achievement of promotion after promotion and the acquisition of wealth and possessions, only to leave it for the widow and children? And in only maybe 20 or 30 years? Wake up! It isn't worth it. Man or woman, you are no different from any other, nor from all other, "sociable" drinkers whose destiny is inevitably an alcoholic or the achievement of a premature demise. Cash in on your present assets while you still have the opportunity to extend your life and your health. Go with your family out to the country and grow your own food, live the life of Freedom and Liberty and Health.—This book is intended for Y O U, too.

You cannot change the effect of alcohol on the human system. Others have tried and have died in the attempt. It seeps through the walls of the stomach and goes directly to the brain area to interfere with its normal activities. What seeps into your liver burns up faster than the fat that is there for the purpose of lubricating your system, thus clogging up your liver. It isn't worth it!

13.
Let's get going—
Live in the City?
Not if I can help it!

What value is your life, without a goal?
What purpose is there in your life on earth?
To scramble for a living, while your soul
Stifled, yearns daily to be free from dearth?

Bestir yourself. There still is lots of room
Upon this glorious land for all of those
Who shattered every thought of pending doom
And sought to achieve the liberty they chose.

The riches which the City life may yeild
Can vanish overnight, as well you know.
While in your cozy country home and field
You have relief from such a frightening woe.

Every good thing for human beings' needs
Almighty God did make provision for,
The earth, the air, the water—even weeds
Are blessings which no person can ignore.

What does man do with all his rent receipts?
Can't go to the Bank and get a loan!
What nonsense! trying to live on such deceits
When that expense can give you a country home!

Choose first the State in which you'd like to live.
Study a Road Map, pick out a good location
Then take the trip. Some Rural land can give
Meaning to Life and a busy long vacation.

N.W.W.

It is now time to give serious thought to becoming
happily settled in your new home on 5 or 10 acres, or

more. What are you going to plant? Why? How much? Learn something about the food you eat and what is involved in the process of growing it, besides plenty of work.

A gardener with his hoe is accomplishing more than the person in his rocking chair just reading about it. If you want to climb a ladder you must start at the bottom. So it is with this project. Reading good books on Gardening and farming and studying Seed catalogs will expand your theoretical knowledge on the subject, but the soil is patiently waiting for you to do something with it.

NOTHING compares to the satisfaction, when planning a meal, of going into your own garden and picking and gathering the finest fresh vegetables and fruits which Almighty God created for your own specific need and sustenance. When you have eaten a few meals composed of organically grown vegetables and fruits, and have eaten sprouted seeds in your salads, you quite naturally wish all your meals could be like these!

There is no reason or justification why you should deprive yourself and your family of the most nutritious food on earth grown in your own garden.

Man was, by Almighty God, intended to live and eat NATURALLY, close to what Nature provided, directly from the source as much as possible. In the beginning man was admonished

Thou shalt eat the herb of the field. In the sweat of thy face shalt thou eat bread. (Genesis 3: 18-19)

But mankind has neglected his nutritional needs and has diverted his attention to acquiring material goods and possessions. In Metropolitan areas we find, today, that such goods and possessions are causing family quarrels and dissension, as a result of financial problems. This is one of the primary sources of tension, resentment and frustration, precursors of most ailments and sickness.

As you watch your earnings disappear into the clouds like a puff of smoke you must be wondering what will happen next. Surely you must be concerned about the chances of you and your family surviving this economic eruption. Life on 5 acres or more, properly planned and managed, can bring you calm confidence, health and economic stability and security.

Whether you happen to be blessed with affluence, or blessed with little or nothing, you must consider these two principles::

The advantages of hard work associated with freedom, health and country living, or

The folly of the gregarious life of the Metropolitan City dweller imprisoned in circumscribed apartment canyons or in the Suburban atmosphere imbued by the four demons:

ENVY VANITY LUST and GREED.

Work on your 5 acres or more, whether physical or mental, will help to activate all your glands. There is no more constructive work than that which results in furnishing you and your family with an abundance of food in the country, in clean, pure air. There is little to be thankful for in the sunset years of your life from having damaged organs in your body from the pollution of a Metropolitan atmosphere and the raucous City noises disrupting the fibers of your brain centers.

The life that IS worthwhile is not the life based on the acquisition of wealth and possessions, because these can vanish overnight, and they all too frequently do.

The life that IS worthwhile is the life of Country Freedom, of independence, close to God and Nature, where you are your own manager and executive, and your success is the direct result of your own efforts and labor.

INTERRUPTION: *I interrupted my typing at this point to go into the house for my breakfast. I frequently get to work as soon as I am up and dressed and an hour or two later I go in to eat my breakfast. This particular interruption is very timely, because in reading the Editorial column of my morning paper, the Arizona Republic, July 3rd 1975, just now, here is part of what its Editor has to say regarding the mental and physical pollution in the City of New York—which applies to nearly every other Metropolitan area:* I quote verbatim:: (Referring to disruptive groups:)

"They are terrorist organizations pure and simple. They live by spreading fear, and threatening death and destruction.

Think for a moment what the New York sanitation workers are doing. New York is a City of 8 million people, crowded together, with thousands dwelling in a single block. They pile up 30,000 tons of garbage a day, and there it stands, decaying in the sun, until it can be collected. It must be collected daily. If permitted to pile up, day after day, 210,000 tons in a single week, an epidemic of fearful proportions, imperiling the lives of all 8 million, would be almost inevitable."

Now please tell me—was this interruption accidental? Not at all. We are living in days when God helps those who help themselves, and I don't mean helping oneself to other people's property, comfort or peace of mind. Self preservation begins BEFORE a calamity strikes. SURVIVAL is the result of being able to foresee coming events which are destructive, and take positive action for your protection AND SURVIVAL.

The home garden in the country, when well planned and well prepared and cared for has proved to be of recreational as well as of health and economic value. With proper planning, your garden can produce vegetables throughout the entire growing season, and you can have enough—and more than enough—to take care of your needs throughout the Winter.

The idea which has been brandished abroad so liberally and persistently, that we are running out of fertile land on which to grow our food, is true, because too much of our soil has been devitalized and ruined by the use of chemical fertilizers, and poisonous sprays.

An entire new generation is today well on its way to maturity, seeking, seeking and seeking—seeking what? Truth, faith, security and self-preservation. Guidance is what they are looking for. Discipline is what they need.

Almighty God is the only source of every good thing that man could want, desire or need. He has created this planet Earth and Humanity on it, for a purpose, not for man to destroy it and himself. Freedom of will and of choice belong to every man, woman and child. It is their Heritage. At the very base of that Heritage is the GOOD EARTH from which comes whatever man needs. Why do you have that gray matter in your skull? It was placed there to enable you to THINK and to plan. Do so, and start NOW.

However, don't start packing yet, ready to move. We still have a few more matters to take into consideration.

14.

Smoking can be Fatal
To Your Marriage

In the beginning God made Man.
  He made a perfect, wholesome body,
Gave him a Garden with one ban,
  Everything faultless, nothing shoddy.

He gave man an order about Food,
  Told him Not to eat one fruit.
Satan told Eve: That fruit is good,
  You cannot die, he'll follow suit.

Many a thousand year went by,
  Then man discovered a new token.
Found a weed that, by and by,
  He lit and puffed and started smokin'.

Now the child of smoking folk
  Is born diseased and maimed and sick,
With every breath he's like to choke
  His folks keep smoking, think it's slick!

Oh you perverted generation,
  Blowing your smoke up to the rafter.
Use your smoking as your ration
  That's awaiting your hereafter.

N.W.W.

Personally, I have no objection to people smoking—in the hereafter. However, while I am still here on this Planet Earth, I demand the right and the privilege of keeping my own lungs as clean and pure as it is humanly possible to do. It is one reason that no amount of money could induce me to live in a Metropolitan City apartment, or work in a large City office building where I would be constantly obliged to breathe the foul tobacco aroma emanating from both men and women in offices and elevators.

Even living in a detached home in the City one cannot escape from the stench of the smoking weed pouring out of the homes of neighbors who smoke, when the wind is blowing from the direction of their house. Their very existence seems to be shrouded in clouds of smoke from the pestiferous weed.

How can anyone obtain any advantage from open windows to obtain fresh air only to become nauseated by one's neighbors' porcine breezes floating in, instead of God's pure atmosphere? It certainly is a problem which only the open spaces of a 5 or 10 acre domain seems able to overcome.

Laws promulgated to stop smoking in public places are virtually useless, because nothing can prevent a smoker from using his weed in his home, in his car or on the streets. This evil will remain with us as long as men and women lose their sense of value of their body and fail to consider their offense against those who do not smoke.

It is generally conceded, today, that one of the abominable crimes is the bringing into this world the body of a baby whose blood stream has been polluted by the nicotine in its mother's blood stream, because of her habit of smoking, particularly during pregnancy.

Happily, there is today a progressively increasing vast number of people who feel the way I do.

A smoker, particularly a chain-smoker, may acquire the vice of burning the weed oblivious of the fact that delinquency has seeped into his or her brain matter and fails to realize how the putrid tobacco smoke permeates everything within its atmosphere.

My sentiments are not illusory, hypothetical nor Utopian. Others, prominent people, thousands of them, are just as strongly opposed to being subjected to the stench of the tobacco weed as I am.

I have received the following from the well known Writer, Mr. Mark Wells, under the heading:

SMOKING CAN BE FATAL * * TO YOUR MARRIAGE—

"Mixed marriages just won't work! It's like trying to mate a giraffe with a kangaroo. That's what Father Noonan says."

"This is what a Catholic girl said to me many years ago. It is an opinion not as strongly held today by priests and pastors. But clergymen, counselors, psychologists are looking more quizzically at another "mixed marriage"—smoker and non-smoker, and particularly if the smoker is the wife. And I am an expert witness on the subject.

I remarried recently. I had been divorced for 9 years. I knew that my wife smoked. I knew that she smoked quite a lot. I lit her cigarettes. I had smoked since I was 15 but had not smoked for 10 years at the time I was married. And never heavily. Not before breakfast. And at times not even until after dinner. My smoking was controllable.

Until we were married I saw my wife for 3 or 4 hours in the evening. I did not know yet that she began smoking when she first awakened—smoking and coughing. Or that she reached for a cigarette any time she woke in the night. It seemed that the need for a cigarette break did not stop during the night.

I hadn't realized that her smoking was incessant and compulsive. And I didn't realize how sensitive I had become to the foul, acrid fumes of cigarettes. I had lived in smoke-free rooms for 10 years—happily. And I had become aware in those years that smoke in a confined area—an airplane, train, restaurant, hotel rooms—had become violently offensive.

Now, of course, there is nothing like a honeymoon to accentuate the problem of a heavy-smoking wife and a non-smoking husband. I found that a honeymoon in a smoke-filled car and smoke-fogged motel rooms was not what I had envisioned. My mild protests were spurned.

"You knew that I smoked before we were married".

Yes, I knew it. But I hadn't considered it. And I didn't know that she smoked THAT much. I didn't know that anyone COULD smoke that much. And the prospect of living in a smokehouse the rest of my life was becoming less and less beguiling. My remonstrances became less mild. And her resentment likewise. She had always been with people who smoked—father, mother, friends, two other husbands. She had never heard smoking questioned and recognized no valid objections to it.

Gradually something filtered through the stench into my mind, something that I believe is making smoking a devisive issue in this country and creating a rift between smokers and non-smokers. I realize that I was not just being irritated by the smoke—eyes, nose, throat and disposition. I was vexed and wroth at my wife's *conduct*. I was making a *moral* judgment against her—a judgement that her action, whatever sanction it had historically, was inconsiderate, offensive, even hostile. I was beginning to look at her noxious habit, not merely as something unpleasant, but as something nasty, ugly, unwholesome, and virtually inexcusable. It was not simply an irritation—it was a grievous fault, a strain, a flaw.

I believe that this is a valid assessment. The sight of a normal person deliberately inflicting on herself these acrid, poisonous fumes is not a pretty one. And loosing this belching inferno on innocent bystanders is unforgivable.

Now, for just a moment, see how detached you can be. Try to believe that you have never heard of a cigarette. You are completely oblivious to the smoking concept. O.K.? Now you see a woman—wife, mother, daughter, friend—put a little white cylinder between her lips—AND SET FIRE TO IT! Then, incredibly, you watch as she sucks at it - hungrily - voraciously - greedily - cheeks taut and then, in a heavy, gasping heave draws it all deep into her lungs and then emits a dense cloud of gray smoke from mouth and nostrils, followed by a wracking paroxysm of coughing. You—eyes smarting, throat burning, nose stinging—- join in the coughing.

You watch in horror and unbelief as this strange rite continues. WHY does she do it—suck in this foul, evil smelling stuff and then spew it out into the air, coughing, choking, snorting? How unfeminine! How unladylike! Is she under some sort of spell? Is it some kind of exorcism? Masochism? Self-flagellation? It can't be for pleasure, certainly. Can it? But look, she grinds out the flaming end of the thing into a receptacle, leaving a smudgy, smelly, odious looking little mess - then - takes another cylinder - puts it in her mouth - and sets it on fire!

This is too much. You flee. Hours later you return, open the door. You reel from the stale, stinking smell that smites you. Later you will learn that this smell will remain. It will become part of the room—part of the house—part of the drapes and other fabrics—part of anything that will absorb nauseous odors. You notice that in several receptacles are ends of the cylinders, crumpled up in ashes, repulsive, abhorrent to the senses.

It didn't seem this way when I began to smoke - when cigarettes were 10 cents or 12 cents a pack. Smoking was glamorous - one of the social graces - and still mostly a masculine prerogative, except for the movie stars - Bette Davis, Crawford, Garbo, the gangsters' moll. But NOT Pickford, Gish or Costello. I remember how handsome John Barrymore looked in

Grand Hotel or Rasputin, smoke streaming from his exquisitely sensitive flared left nostril (profile shot, of course) (No one knew for sure whether he HAD a right nostril). But, of course, we never saw Barrymore's lungs."

15.
Dehydration of Foods for Survival

Wilful waste results in woeful want.
  Don't be a burden to your Government.
Let fear of dole your conscience daunt.
  Food conservation learn to implement.

When in your fertile garden, in due Season,
  The food you grow is abundant, at its peak
Of ripeness. From such harvest you have reason
  To gather what you don't eat, week by week.

That is the surplus you should dehydrate
  To build a store of food for other climes,
When foresight will reward you at the rate
  That you foretell your need for scarcer times.

Food that is dried by proper, correct means
  Retains its life no less than all Enzymes
In such a way no other method seems
  To keep to preserve the food betimes.

N.W.W.

I doubt if, in human history, there ever was such a need to store up food as there is in this present day and generation.

For the past half century there has been a cumulative effort to force the increase in the production of food, and to develop ways and means by which the food will keep indefinitely, without spoiling.

Immense sums of money have been expended to try to do something that the very simple system of proper DEHYDRATION can do.

The food problem is, actually, the major worry of knowledgeable legislative bodies. The consumption of food by Metropolises and Megalopolises staggers the imagination. Perhaps the volume of City garbage may be an indication of the end-product of this problem. The City of New York is reported to have some 30,000 tons of garbage to collect and dispose of every day. Do you realize what a colossal amount of garbage that is? In pounds this amounts to some 960 MILLION pounds of garbage a day, and New York City's population is figured at about 8 MILLION people. It has been estimated that New Yorkers waste about 22% of their food, which goes to fill their garbage cans.

Can you for a moment visualize 8,000,000 people cooped up at the rate of 1,000 or more in a single block of apartments? One of New York's food baskets is the New Jersey area, the State immediately adjoining the City, to the South and West.

At this writing, only a week or two have passed since the State of New Jersey had a devastating volume of rain which caused many, many millions of dollars of damage to its crops—crops which were intended mostly to feed the bulging population of New York City.

There is NOTHING that either you or I can do for that edematous Metropolitan City, nor for any edematous Metropolis. They must be allowed to lie in the bed they made for themselves, until individuals, as such, awaken to their predicament and take the necessary steps to prepare for SURVIVAL.

Dehydration of raw foods is the key to survival, but

one must realize what that involves in the volume of food to be dehydrated in relation to the dried food resulting from that process. The water content of vegetables and fruits varies from about 50% to as much as 95%. 90% of this water must be evaporated in the dehydration process to leave the nutrition-containing fibers available for eventual use as food.

Consider the colossal saving of space in storing dehydrated foods. One ton of an average assortment of fresh vegetables in their whole, freshly gathered state would weigh 2,000 pounds. When dehydrated these would weigh only about 250 pounds, to 300 pounds, requiring only a small space for storage in your food cellar on your 5 or 10 acres in the country.

Dehydration of foods has been known and practiced for centuries, probably millennia. Today, however, we have a tremendous advantage over people of the age before electricity. Today electricity makes dehydration of foods possible with the least effort and expense, and greater control over the process.

The matter of converting dehydrated foods back to their near-normal state is comparatively simple, particularly if you have your own water distilling equipment. To re-constitute your dehydrated foods you soak them in either cold or warm distilled water for anywhere from one or two hours, to overnight, depending on the kind of food you are re-constituting. The food is then delicious. If you will warm the distilled water to about 125^{0}F the process of reconstitution will be speeded up amazingly.

In contrast to the dehydrators of many years ago, the dehydration of foods has today become big business, with the consequent manufacture and sale of many thousands of dehydrating units for the home.

Because of the variety of designs and structure of home dehydrating equipment, everyone interested should make his own investigation and come to his own decision as to the best one suited to his needs, conditions and circumstances.

Some of the important things to look for are the method of heating and of the control of the heat, which should not exceed 120 degrees F. Then you should look for the means used for the circulation of air. This is very important because the heat should be evenly distributed through and between the trays on which the food is being placed.

The greatest advantage of having your own Dehydrator is that when the vegetables and fruits in your own garden have reached the peak of their ripeness you are able to dehydrate everything that you do not use for your immediate meals. There should be no loss or waste from your garden. All of your surplus, properly cared for and stored, will be better than money in the Bank.

Depending on the size of your garden, one growing season could readily enable you to store enough dehydrated food, not only to feed, but to NOURISH your family for months ahead.

Unlike canned foods, dehydration enables you to retain all the nutrition contained in your vegetables and fruits, all your Minerals, Vitamins and Enzymes. Furthermore, it retains these vital properties in their live organic state.

Besides your vegetables and fruits you will no doubt have an abundant supply of HERBS in your garden. What a cornucopia you can build up for your Herb Tea requirements!

For instance, Mint. What greater treat than to be able to make a pot of Mint Tea on a cold Winter day, or ice-cold on a hot Summer day, made from the fragrant plants which you have grown yourself.

Or consider Comfrey, that valuable vegetable-herb which has been neglected by housewives for so long. The whole plant, leaves and root, can be effectively dehydrated and a plentiful supply made available for a beverage, for use for its healing qualities, and in salads.

Meat is something we do not use in our family. However, by far the majority of people are meat eaters. We neither condemn nor condone the eating of meat. Each must eat according to the best of his knowledge, taste and physical needs. The Holy Bible, of course, in the Book of Leviticus (Chapter 11) gives in detail the Dietary Laws promulgated by Almighty God for clean and unclean foods which, for very good reasons, man may eat or not eat, as he chooses.

Unquestionably, the ingestion of meat creates excessive amounts of uric acid which is the forerunner of nerve and muscular afflictions, such as rheumatism, neuritis, and the like.

For those who like to eat meat without thought or qualms, dehydration is invaluable for preserving it. Raw meat can be cut into slices which readily respond to dehydration. In this manner it can be kept for longer periods than can the frozen kind. Furthermore, what happens in "Meat Freezing Compartments" when electricity fails for a prolonged period of time? The answer to this question is obvious. A prolonged electrical power shortage can play havoc with a supply of meat upon which people are depending. Freezers, both in the home and commercial ones, are fallible and only dependable so long as the electrical system is operating up to par. You don't have that problem when meat and other foods are dehydrated and stored properly with care and attention to the circumstances surrounding such storage, which is not dependent on electricity.

16.
Dexter—
The Dwarf Irish Cattle

England was angry. Ireland had vexed her.
Why didn't M.P.'s study small Irish cattle?
They would, with surprise, have discovered the small Irish
Dexter
And gone into business instead of going into battle!

A fairly large herd of Dexters on a good British farm
From history then could remove of contention the bone.
The Irish should then be no further cause for alarm
And the small Dexter cattle would also come into its own.

Some foresighted Farmers brought some small Dexter cattle
From Irish soil into our Great U.S.A.,
Now, without argument, back-talk, fussing or prattle
They KNOW Dexter milk and small steers are very good pay.

They have discovered that the small Dexter cow's milk
Is homogenized directly as it comes from the udder,
Unlike the milk from Jerseys, Holsteins and their ilk.
Now they sell Dexter milk without qualms and with
nary a shudder.

If today I were blessed with a farm and few acres, to battle
With soil, with Guineas, with poultry and with my spouse,
I'd choose me a nice little herd of small Dexter cattle,
They're easy to keep and they don't need much land to
browse.

N.W.W.

The secret of growing good nutritional food lies in the presence of plenty of organic fertilizer and compost, in your soil.

You are going to need a great deal of ORGANIC fertilizer and poultry droppings for your compost.

The question of fertilizer is of vital importance, not only for your own compost and for your own soil, but farmers and gardeners EVERYWHERE are potential buyers of good organic fertilizer. The land in virtually every part of this country—no less than in other countries—has been to a great extent sterilized by the application of chemical fertilizers, and ruined for the production of Mineral and Vitamin replete food.

Cattle and horses furnish excellent fertilizer manure—there is hardly any better. On any kind of a Mini-farm such cattle as Holsteins, Guernseys, even - Jerseys, are almost too large to be practical. There are two or three breeds which are naturally small, which would enable the small farmer to keep them in reasonable numbers.

HERE IS THE CATTLE I WOULD CHOOSE

I have just read a most interesting and enlightening article in COUNTRYSIDE Magazine of August 1975 which I consider so excellent and practical that I want to quote from it. It is written by Don Piehota, P.O. Box 597, Portland, Penna. 18351. *Don Piehota writes:*

"For a year now we have owned a herd of at least 12 cattle which, along with two horses, subsist on 11 acres of pasture for more than half the year. These are not starving skeletons, but fat, frisky Irish Dexter cows and bulls—the smallest breed of cattle.

We had only expected to start out on 2 or 3 cows, but the advantages of 5 or 6 soon became obvious and, then, why not include the bull and that last heifer. I thought there should definitely be a future for cows that are belt-high compared to the average man. The smallest breed of cattle is certainly in direct opposition to the old "bigger and better" creed preached so often in this country.

To the guy with 2 or 3 acres this could mean a hungry, hapless 1200 lb. Holstein penned up on an acre. But, put a 600 lb. Dexter on that acre and she looks like a contented cow in a pasture.

So, we have a mixed bag—ranging from 32" high Lonely Squaw (about 500 lbs.) to 41" Ariel Mary weighing at least 650 lbs. Our bull, Brady's Run Navigator, is belt-high or about 3 feet even, and is very docile and easy going. Summer of '74 saw the addition of four calves to the herd and this Spring 4 more with 2 more due by the end of the Summer. We have sold a cow and a heifer for the price they merit, and interest in our area is growing.

Back in December 1973 my wife and I decided to stock our 12 acre farmette with sheep, but there was an episode which decided us against it. A flock of 40 sheep a few miles North of us was wiped out by a pair of dogs. I had always had a preference for cattle, but the popular breeds such as Jerseys are delicate and the bulls have a bad reputation. Also my past experience with Angus proved to me they are difficult and intractable. We wanted something easily contained by 3 or 4 strands of barbed wire, docile, small enough to keep several on our acreage, and very hardy. Both my wife and I work, and we frankly prefer to find other uses for our money than Vet bills and fancy feeds.

My research in the local Library bore fruit when I ran across material on Irish Dexter cattle. They are dual purpose, meaning they are good milkers and fatten well for slaughter. They originated in Western Ireland where the soil is poor and the land was divided into little rental crofts (farms) of a few acres each. Pasture was poor and small—certainly no setting for a large cow giving many gallons of milk a day in turn for eating everything four acres could produce.

About 200 years ago someone referred to a small black cow, common in that area, which was kept out of doors on pasture all year. I understand "dexter" is the Irish word for small and dark. There were terribly poor breeding practices in those days and only in this century has any attempt been made to upgrade breeding practices and choice of breeding stock. The worst estimate would be that 10% of the regular, larger type of calves are born defective or dead. Only one person out of all the Irish Dexter owners we have met ever had that experience. This improvement is, no doubt, due to modern breeding practices now employed. Some of the large cattle have a high rate of sterility, others have serious complications in delivery, etc. These problems are largely avoided by buying a cow with a reputation as a proven breeder in any breed. The cost is greater, of course.

Our experience with Dexters should be of interest, particularly since we break some of the rules. Along with the requirement that the animals be docile, economical and trouble-free, twice-a-day milking was out of the question. We devised a method which would allow us to miss milking entirely for a day or two if necessary. Any dairy farmer will tell you that one must be a slave to 2 milkings daily or run the risk of serious problems. We fell back on a method I am sure was used by the pioneers. You see, the dairy farmer's problem is that the cow is totally dependent upon him to be milked, since the calf had become veal cutlets a week or two after birth.

Our technique involves allowing the calf and cow to spend all day together, and then bringing the cows to be milked, into the shed in the evening where they remain till the next morning. They then have a full udder and are easy to milk. We do not need to strip the udder, since the calf is waiting for momma at the door and he will take care of that. Should we be away for a day or two, the cows stay out with the calves and no harm is done. Of course instead of getting gallons at a milking, we only take quarts, but there are only 5 of us, so 4 quarts a day is more than enough for our drinking, cooking and cottage cheese.

Our milking operation is very relaxed, flexible, and

certainly could be considered "trouble-free". Incidentally, Dexter milk is naturally homogenized—like goats' milk.

The question of economy in Dexters has been solved to my satisfaction after having Wintered 12 head. By early December we were feeding 3 bales of hay and 2 large buckets of ear corn which we chopped in pieces for easier eating. We ran through 2 tons of ear corn by the end of January, and brought all 12 cattle through the rest of the Winter on 4 bales of hay a day. A couple of the smaller animals were quite fat. Of course they had free run of all the pasture and were very busy picking over the greens ignored in the Fall.

It sounds hard to believe that a cow exists requiring only one-third of a bale of hay a day and the privilege of picking over the pasture and brush, to get her through the Winter.

A person with 3 1/2 to 4 acres of pasture-land could easily pasture 2 cows and their calves for about 7 months with no supplementary feeding. It would be best if the pasture were divided down the middle with an electric fence. This allows the cattle to feed several weeks on one half while the other half grows. In the Winter take the fence down and allow the cattle to roam over all the pasture, picking over the Summer left-overs. If properly planned, one cow will always be milking and the cost would be 5 or 6 months' supply of hay plus a little corn.

I have estimated the following expenses if one wishes to keep 2 cows: $180 for 220 bales of hay, $40 for ear corn (1/2 ton) and miscellaneous, such as halter, Vet fees, etc., at $30. The total expense should be close to $250. The calves, (probably a castrated bull-calf and a heifer) would be "Wintered", and the following Summer the heifer, ready to be bred at 14 or 15 months, would be worth $250. The little steer, at 17 or 18 months, provides $250 worth of grass-fed beef. Dexters mature so fast that at 12 or 13 months they are practically as tall as their parents and more than half as heavy. Our little steer should weigh around 450 lbs. at slaughter, yielding almost 250 lbs. of meat. So far, the $250 expense has already yielded $500. In addition, there is the value of the milk. On our trouble-free method even one gallon a day for 310 days is worth at least $350. It is certainly a decent hobby that provides such a handsome return.

It is very pleasant and satisfying to watch our animals eat, calve, and remind us of the basics of Nature. It is rewarding to feel a little more self-sufficient and a little less at the mercy of the economic forces beyond our control. When dairy drivers go on strike mothers everywhere panic, but with a serene and loving look at the family, we pick up the bucket and go out to milk. In that little shed next to the 1 1/2 acre paddock, the only cow that makes sense to keep is a 39-inch-tall Irish Dexter."
(Thus writes Don Piehota, the author of the foregoing classic.)

You must understand, of course, that we do not eat meat, but the vast majority of people do. Our evaluation of cattle and other livestock on the farm is for the purpose of obtaining as much barn and stable manure for the compost, at the least possible expense. I believe that Dexter cattle is an answer to this problem.

After reading and studying the foregoing dissertation on the small Irish Dexter cattle, you should realize the fertilizer value of such a herd on your 5 or 10 acres or more.

While horse manure is an excellent fertilizer for your compost and for your soil, I do not wish to go into the matter of keeping horses. They are without question very useful—I should say extremely useful—animals to have on your place, particularly if your automobile means of transportation fails you and you may have to ride horseback into town. However, for all other practical purposes there is usually no income which can usually be expected from keeping a horse. Furthermore, if the horse is used to any extent, it needs to be shod at intervals of every few weeks, and horseshoeing is expensive, nowadays. So, I will leave the equestrian matter for you to look into and investigate from some other source.

17.
Pygmy Goats?
Goats?—Diminutive Goats!!

Hi! Little Nannie, what is your role?
Let's put on your leash and go for a stroll.
As we wander along, me with my pride,
I glance down at my pygmy as she struts at my side.

These tiny wee goats are such pets to keep.
They clean up the brush with never a peep.
They're indeed very clean as a natural habit.
They're quick and as lively as a frisky young rabbit.

They're easy to feed, but remember you ought 'ter
Have plenty supply of pure, clean, fresh water.
They're easy to milk, too, and give plenty of it,
So what you don't drink you can sell at a profit.

N.W.W.

One of the necessary chores on any country domain is to control brush and weeds in areas which are not generally cultivated. On our Ranch in the Ozarks of Arkansas we simply HAD to have some means to control the underbrush or it would grow to a height of 6 to 8 feet. When we first moved there, after the place had been unoccupied for several months, the weeds and brush were from 5 to 8 feet high and we had to use a weed cutter, known as a brush-hog, attached to our tractor to cut it down. Thereafter we bought half a dozen goats — regular standard size goats, and about 3 dozen Toulouse geese to do the work. Between them they did a splendid job, the goats with the brush and the geese with weeding.

On account of my experience I consider it good advice to seriously consider the addition of goats to your domain. They are excellent livestock and well worth considering.

In this connection I have recently learned of diminutive, dwarf or pygmy goats that are generally no higher than 18 to 22 inches.

These tiny goats are just as efficient as their larger counterparts and, I am of the opinion that they could become particularly useful pets. Had I known about them when we had our Arkansas farm I would certainly have been tempted to have a flock of them. When the time comes for me to get back on a farm these little pets will be among the first of the livestock that I will want to have.

I first learned of PYGMY GOATS when I read an article in the COUNTRYSIDE Magazine of August 1975 by Eva Rappaport. I considered this article so important that I immediately contacted both the Editor of the COUNTRYSIDE Magazine and Mrs. Eva Rappaport at her "Kings Valley Animal Family Farm" in Monmouth, Oregon for permission to reproduce it in this book, to which they both consented. The article speaks for itself, and here it is, in toto:

MINI GUIDE TO PYGMY GOATS

Pygmy Goats are no longer considered exotic oddities. Now recognized as a distinct, genetically stable species (derived mainly from Swedish seed stock imported in 1959), pygmy goats will soon be registered as the sixth major goat breed in the U.S.

The American pygmy goat is genetically small, muscular, compactly built, cobby and paunchy, and measures between 18 and 22 inches at the withers. The head is medium long, level and dished. Colors range from silver to agouti (salt and pepper). There are characteristic lighter markings on the muzzle, erect ears, broad forehead, and around the large, well spaced eyes. Pygmy goats have black socks and hooves and a dorsal stripe. Coat length and density vary with climates, making the pygmy goat at home in the desert or northern tundra.

Pygmy goats mature early, can be bred young, bear one to four offspring every nine to 12 months, and are excellent parents. Females produce up to four pounds of delicious milk per day. Its flavor is consistently sweet and nutty, regardless of feed consumed, and has a butterfat content of 6-9%. While the lactation period of pygmy goats is shorter than that of other breeds, staggered breeding of two to three pygmy can keep a small family supplied with milk throughout the year.

Pygmy goats are efficient browsers. They clear brush better than big scrub goats because of their impressive agility at climbing and jumping, even into and out of trees. Yet they will stay in fenced areas when in the company of other animals. However, a lonely pygmy goat will leap over a five-foot fence to seek companionship and will follow its owner like a loyal dog.

Pygmy goats not only make excellent pets, but they earn their keep as providers and gardeners, and as research subjects as well. They are intelligent, sociable, verbal, alert, cooperative, and docile. They like children, cats and dogs — in fact, any creature with whom they have had contact while still young. They will readily walk with you on leash or off, in town or countryside. A pygmy will come to the call of its name to take its place on the milking stanchion and can be milked by hand or machine. With food rewards, pygmies are quick to learn all kinds of routines.

Four pygmy goats can live contentedly in a draft-free 8' x 10' shed. If possible, they should also have access to an adjoining exercise yard that provides protection from direct sun and has elevated areas for climbing and sleeping. Fresh water, hay and salt-vitamin-mineral mix should be available at all times. Grain is required only during lactation and for the month preceding it. The buck's ration of two cups per day should be doubled during the breeding season.

The basic diet of pygmies is roughage, in the form of grass hay, alfalfa hay, bark, brush, and/or dry leaves. Females in milk eat about three cups of mixed grains twice a day, fed from a pan while being milked. A prepared goat chow is favored, but a home-mixed e-quivalent is acceptable.

Newborn pygmy kids will nurse their dams within an hour after birth. During the first four days, kids obtain an immunity to disease through the colostrum milk. After that, they can be bottle-fed three times a day on goat milk, evaporated milk diluted 1:2 with water, or milk replacers warmed to 100+ degrees and offered in 10 oz. pop bottles with soft lamb nipples attached. Kids will quickly master the Lambar, which is a great time saver when more than two kids are to be fed. By two months of age when kids will be eating hay and rolled oats, two bottles of skimmed milk a day will suffice. Just before weaning at four months, the milk can be diluted and the quantity gradually reduced. Hand-raising kids, while time-consuming, greatly promotes lasting sociability.

Pygmy goats are genetically horned, but dis-budding with an electric dehorning iron at one week of age will prevent later accidents and damage. Ear tat-

toos assure positive identification for registration. Vaccination with tetanus antitoxin, Bo-Se 7-in-11 (C&D) toxoid, and ovine mixed bacterin should be administered routinely.
End of article.

Here you have Mrs. Rappaport's interesting and enlightening experience in breeding and raising these little pets.

While I differ with Mrs. Rappaport's experience expressed in the last few lines of her article, I do grant that her work is based on the orthodox method of immunizing animals. In the few years during which we had and bred our standard size goats we never gave them any processed food—such as evaporated or other types of processed milk. Nor did we use any vaccination or other drugs or medication, and we had a very healthy lot of goats and kids when we sold them at the time we left the farm.

Of course it must be borne in mind that the Walker Program considers anything that is not strictly natural as being contrary to the basic principles of HEALTH once the body has been brought up to as near a state of cleanliness as possible, and has been nourished on raw foods, as much as possible.

18.
—Guinea Fowl—

Oh Guinea fowl, Oh Guinea fowl,
  How happy you seem around our field and stream.
The predator jungle creatures that prowl.
  With Africa's wilderness, now but a dream.

Thank God for your loud sounding squawk and alarm.
  When strangers and foxes and cats and a hawk
Come snooping around to do us some harm
  You're always alert with your warning and squawk.

We prize you, you Guineas, for all you are worth.
  We enjoy the sight of seeing you around.
You eat up the bugs and clean up the Earth
  Of pestiferous insects when these abound.

N.W.W.

A flock of Guinea fowls surpasses any other live-stock in its all around efficiency. The Guinea will, from morning till night, find and eat up every kind of insect and pest that has the tendency to be harmful to vegetables and fruits, as quickly as it can find them. They are not choosey as to the kind and type of pest.

As watch-dogs—well, with a flock of Guineas around the place you don't need a watch-dog to warn you of trespassers. The moment a stranger, or any predatory animal or bird puts in an appearance, they sound the alarm, and a very effective alarm at that. They are also quite a chattering bird, but one gets used to their chatter when one appreciates all their wonderful qualities and virtues.

No domestic fowl can be raised so cheaply, both in the matter of feed and of housing. The reason for this is that the Guinea is the nearest to the wild of all domestic fowl. Guineas are exceptionally clean birds. They thrive best when they can have almost unlimited range. They require clean water. When left to themselves they can readily procure these essentials. By bearing these requirements in mind and observing them, Guineas can be raised in captive conditions most satisfactorily and profitably.

Originally, Guineas were exported from Africa, where this bird is still prized and hunted as a game bird.

In the United States of America there are only an estimated 3 million Guineas throughout the country. Any one who raises poultry can raise Guineas as his own game bird for their egg production, for the table or for market, without having to get a Game License. While originally the Guinea was a wild game bird, (and it still is wild in the jungles of Africa) it has over the years been domesticated so that it can be bred and reared in any barnyard. Although they do somewhat better on free range, they accept a certain degree of confinement so long as they can have access to plant insects and thus help control the plagues which beset the vegetable garden and field crops. Even when allowed quite free range, they will come home to roost if grain feed is consistently available upon their return.

The Guinea hen must be allowed to choose her own nesting place. It is therefore advisable to have as many low bushes and shrubs around your acres as possible, so that you can find where they lay their eggs. Often several Guinea hens will lay eggs in the same nest.

A friend of ours whose farm was only a few miles from our place in the Ozarks of Arkansas, kept a large flock of Guineas which were allowed to roam all over their place. Regularly, at about 4 o'clock every afternoon, their Guineas would come strolling back to the house for their grain supper, and I loved to watch them. I had ordered a bunch of their keets, the Guinea baby chicks, but we had to come back to Phoenix before they were available, which grieved me. We wanted to raise them for their alarm proclivities, as we had many predators, such as racoons, etc., which bothered our chickens, Bantams and geese.

For some unknown reason, Guineas are less subject to the afflictions which so often beset poultry. They are more hardy.

If you are among those who do not eat flesh food, you must bear in mind that most of the population of the world does eat meat. In this respect I should point out that edible birds, such as poultry, pheasants, partridge, quail and particularly Guineas, have a more digestible and less acid-forming flesh than the flesh of cattle. Nevertheless, when bird flesh is eaten it should be eaten judiciously and in moderation.

Considering the financial angle of your farm operation, you should take into account the profitable income which Guineas can provide. Guinea hens are consistent layers during the Summer, beginning from April, through the Fall. It has been found to be a better practice to raise your own birds rather than to buy those which are mature. In that case, the early - April and May - eggs should be used for your incubator. It takes from 26 to 28 days for these eggs to hatch.

You may find your market for your surplus eggs by starting a local classified advertising campaign. News quickly spreads in a country community.

Guinea Fowls Profitable

In years past about the only Guinea fowls seen were a pair or so among the flocks of hens of farm poultry raisers.

These lonely specimens were kept mostly because they were so handsomely feathered, and roamed afield so far that their feeding cost was nil; or perhaps the farmers realized their value as "watch dogs" over all the feathered flock.

No attempt was made to breed them in numbers; they were rarely eaten on the home table and never were offered for sale. Guineas were not advertised, nor written about, nor pictured, and never exhibited at a poultry or game bird show. In fact, for generations they have been "the forgotten bird."

Only of late has there been an interest manifest in raising Guinea Fowl commercially,— and as yet this phase of Guinea raising is in its infancy.

However, it has been noticable for several years that Guineas are coming into favor,—and well they may, as they have much to recommend them to the farmer, the hatchery man and to ranches where Guinea raising may be entered into on a large scale.

Guinea fowls are not subject to many of the diseases that affect other poultry. This is of itself a great factor in their favor. They require very little and inexpensive housing; an open shed is more to their liking than a modern poultry house, except in extremely cold winter weather in a northern climate. Their favorite roosting place at night is high up in trees or on the ridge-board of barn roofs.

Their fresh-air habits and roaming disposition make them extremely hardy. They are adaptable to almost any climate.

Guineas have earned their reputation of being the best of watchdogs. They are sensitive to the approach of any strange animals, such as hawks, foxes, cats, dogs, skunks, etc. and are on the alert day and night to sound the alarm when anything unusual is going on. Not only do they make an alarm that usually drives animal marauders away, but they will put up a fight, and invariably come off victors. Poultry raisers,—hen, turkeys, waterfowl, can well afford to keep Guineas if for no other reason than to protect their flocks. If any human prowler comes around in the night, Guineas will set up such a screeching that the intruders will sneak away to where no Guineas are on guard.

The habits of Guineas living on buts, worms, week seeds, and leaves of plants, as do wild game, gives their meat a distinctive "gamey flavor", and the birds are largely used, especially when young, as a substitute for game birds when the latter are out of season, hard to procure, or extremely expensive. Young Guineas are becoming more and more in demand by hotels, restaurants, clubs, lodge, society, school and other banquets. The prices are very satisfactory to the growers. Many breeders of Guineas are now taking advantage of this outlet for all the birds they can raise; the demand is permanent and increasing.

Formerly none but the handsome Pearled variety were raised, but now the white plumage ones are as popular as the other. A few fancy varieties are raised as ornamental, but the Pearl and White are the only varieties bred in large numbers.

Guineas require a little different treatment and care than other breeds of poultry. They require range when raised in large numbers, but small flocks can be raised on farms where other fowls are kept; and even backyard conditions have been found successful. Where Guineas are allowed to range they fend for themselves, with so little commercial feed necessary that they are the most profitable variety of domestic fowls. The poultryman who will undertake to raise Guineas on a commercial scale is quite likely to diminish his hen flock and increase his Guinea flock to increase his profits. There is a growing demand for breeding stock, hatching eggs, and "keets" as the young Guinea chicks are called.

—V.H. in Rural New Yorker.

Please Note:: This entire foregoing section from its heading "Guinea Fowls Are Profitable", down to the immediately preceding paragraph, is taken from page

39 of the book "Guinea Fowl" by permission of Mr. Loyl Stromberg, owner of the Copyright of that book. I take this opportunity to express my appreciation to Mr. Stromberg for his consent, and for the use of the illustrations which accompany this article.

Before you take your first step into buying or raising Guineas, I would urge you to read and STUDY that excellent book "Guinea Fowl" by Van-Hoesen-Stromberg.

19.
The Hen is valuable besides being an egg's way to make another egg

(Samuel Butler. 1835-1902)

A riddle that some people reverse
Is heard from far and from near.
Forget it, I beg,
If the chicken or egg
Was the first of the two to appear.

Today it's revealed very well:
The Life of every cell
In bird as in cod
Was created by God,
As in Adam, before he fell.

N.W.W.

Because I waxed so eloquent on my predilection for Guinea Fowl, do not for one moment think that I, in any way, underrate the importance of the feathered flock we generally classify as POULTRY. To underestimate hens and roosters would indeed justify you in figuring that I don't know what I am talking about.

The two principle reasons for raising POULTRY are, first of all for their extremely valuable droppings, which are an excellent fertilizer. Mixed with barnyard manure these two fertilizing items combine to form the finest kind of organic composting fertilizer.

In the second place, poultry eggs are an excellent source of protein. Two eggs can furnish all the necessary or supplementary protein that an adult requires to maintain his protein level. Such eggs, I should emphasize, are mainly of supreme importance when the fowl have been allowed to roam freely on the ground, in the garden, in the field or even in the woods. Another essential prerequisite is for the eggs to be fertilized. For this purpose there should be one rooster for every 10 to 15 hens in each flock. The germination of eggs is important, because otherwise many of the trace elements which depend on the interchange of the poultry's sex glands' activity would be missing. Trace elements are hard enough to get in the regular run of food for humans, particularly when food has not been grown on properly composted soil.

I therefore frankly recommend and advise the maintaining of a poultry flock commensurate with the size of the estate and with the needs of the family.

When it comes to the matter of choosing any kind or particular kind or breed of birds, the list of the many varieties available is unbelievably long.

I have before me at this moment, for example, a book entitled STANDARD OF POULTRY PERFECTION which describes itself as "A complete description of all recognized varieties of fowls". And that is just about what it is. I keep this book in my library because, frankly, I would like to keep a few score of the many varieties. The book has some 620 pages or more, illustrating in great deal, with pictures of both hens and roosters, nearly every bird described in it.

Besides the more familiar breeds, such as Leghorns, Rhode Islands, Minorcas, New Hampshires, Wyandottes, Cornish, Barred Rocks, Araucanas, Jersey Giants, I would so much like to have a pair of the beautiful Silver Duckwings and breed some chickens, and perhaps Malays, Cubalayas, and some majestic Silvergray Dorkins, and some White Crested Black Polish with their astonishing busby-like head gear. I feel I could have lots of fun raising each of these. As a matter of fact I even joined the S.P.P.A. — Society for the Preservation of Poultry Antiquities—which, among other interesting activities, encourages better breeding and helps Members locate Rare Stock, issuing Bulletins to its Members.

Bear in mind that poultry eggs can be a profitable part of your farm budget. If you can grow most of the feed that your flock will need, you will reduce the upkeep considerably. You can figure that a good laying hen can lay 250 to 300 eggs a year, so that every dozen hens you have would yield between 250 and 300 dozen eggs a year.

You know how much you are paying to your market or Supermarket now for every dozen eggs you buy. Compare that to the contrasting small cost of keeping your hens which under proper conditions would lay eggs most of the year.

In regard to the fertilizing value of your poultry, this would be much greater than what you could expect from GUINEAS, as your poultry would be housed in your poultry house, while your Guineas would most likely roost elsewhere, except in very cold weather.

If you plan to raise your own chickens, you will need an incubator. You will find that there is quite a variety to choose from, including one that turns the eggs automatically. All one has to do is put any number up to 70 or 80 hens' eggs in it and, checking its operation at frequent intervals — every day or two — in a matter of three weeks you may find yourself with a nice flock of tiny day-old baby chicks. If you wish to hatch Guinea eggs, which are a little smaller, you could put in about 100 eggs, which would take 26-28 days to hatch.

How thrilling it is to set a lot of eggs, and in due course, be regaled by Nature with precious, lively little chicks!

Buff Orpington

Silver Leghorn

Black Langshans

Buff Laced Polish

White Laced Red Cornish

Golden Duckwing Leghorn

20.
The Bee
The Beehive and the Honey

They bring sweetness, they earn Money.
  My, Oh my, what a dream
  To be a part of such a team!

To be busy as a Bee,
  A busy, busy little Bee
Flying hither, flitting thither,
  Flowers almost every whither.
Yellow flower-, purple flower,
  Flowers of nearly every color.

One by one she finds the pollen,
  Pollen borrowed, pollen stolen,
To her beehive straight she flies
  With those tiny unerring eyes.
There the pollen turns to honey
  Which we buy with hard-earned money.

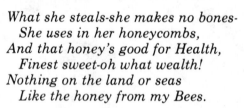

What she steals-she makes no bones-
  She uses in her honeycombs,
And that honey's good for Health,
  Finest sweet-oh what wealth!
Nothing on the land or seas
  Like the honey from my Bees.

Little boys and little girls
  Should value honey more than pearls
Honey for your boys and girls
  Is far more precious than your pearls.
Teach the children to keep Bees,
  They won't go flying overseas:

N.W.W.

Honey is recognized as the most healthy and
beneficial sweetening which the Good Lord has

provided for us. For thousands of years this has been a recognized fact. It is the quickest and most efficient generator of energy - sustained energy, for the human body. It gives you a lift without a letdown.

Athletes in every field of sport obtain a surprising amount of sustained energy by taking one or two tablespoonfuls of honey before starting an event.

Using honey for sweetening every kind of food or beverage is recognized as the intelligent way to appease the taste and benefit the body. Every country home with one or more acres should have beehives, and this makes an excellent project for young people.

This subject is so colossal in its breadth and scope that the problem is not what to say, but where to draw the line.

It's great to gain your own experience (which is usually acquired the hard way) and it is even greater to have the ability to benefit and profit from the experience of others.

When I decided to put some beehives on my farm in the Ozarks of Arkansas, the first thing I did was to look through Bee Journals and Magazines, and I subscribed to GLEENINGS IN BEE CULTURE (published by the A.I. Root Company in Medina, Ohio, 44256). My subscription ran for the best part of three years, and that was quite a number of years ago. I gained a great deal of help from what I learned in that Magazine. I also used the services of many Bee Supply Houses which advertised therein. It really helped me a great deal.

Unquestionably, bees are the farmer's and the gardener's best investment. No hired man could work so long and so hard, and no machinery could work as efficiently with so little upkeep. Wherever there are bees, flowers, fruits and vegetables must abound, because they are vital to pollination.

The most valuable part of the bees' work is to transfer pollen from one flower to another to fertilize it. In botanical language, pollination is the transfer of pollen from the androecium to the gynoecium. This is language with which bees are very familiar! The lack of adequate pollination results not only in a small yield, but also in small or misshapen fruits. Today there are Beekeepers whose sole business is to specially pollinate large acreages where vast commercial production of fruits and vegetables is carried on, and the Packing Houses pay a premium for this work. It is as important as all that!

For little people like you and me this general pollination work is of more than passing interest. It proves the need for the farmer or gardener within our range of operation, to have his own beehives, in addition to the fun, pleasure and independence which accrues from taking care of bees and using the honey they yield.

Some years ago I read a very interesting account in the Magazine GLEANINGS In Bee Culture, of a California Dentist afflicted with what he called APICULTITIS. Apiculture is the name for Beekeeping. I want to give you the gist of his account as he wrote it, and I quote:

"People are surprised at my answer to their question of how long I have kept bees. Fifty-four years! I was just a child when I played helping a Minister take care of his hives. That did it to me. Another friend, the Sunday School Superintendent, gave me a hive of my own. My big thrill came when I took off my first honey. It was so white and it was perfectly capped. My Dad raved because it looked so nice, and my happiness was complete.

Moving and school made some voids in my bee activities. It didn't take too long until I was back at it again - infecting a neighbor also with the Bee Disease.

My present hives have had to be moved several times since my home town of Pasadena continues to grow. Finally bees were voted out of town completely, but that hadn't stopped me. Letters were sent to the City Directors telling them the value of bees before they were banned but the pressure was on and they had to comply. This put us out in the country to BEE, my neighbor and me. He is bitten as badly as I am. I don't intend to treat the APICULTITIS."
End of quote.

Honey of course has been familiar and a favorite since Almighty God created plants and flowers, and people who enjoyed the sweetness of life. Without question honey deserves its lyric eloquence and its healing reputation.

Some years ago Dr. Stanley Coppock, Entomologist with the New Mexico State University stated that work done at the University of Arizona shows that honey has an anti-bacterial action similar to penicillin without its side-effects. We frequently get reports from people who have used honey in one way or another for ailments and injuries, with excellent results.

Here is another interesting report that came to me some time ago. "The Brotherhood Organization of the Bee Church had a honey of a banquet last Tuesday night. Three long tables, all decked in white, with plates and napkins, knives and forks, goblets of ice water and 12 large bowls of good looking comb honey—4 bowls on each table. The meeting was called to order. A prayer was offered. The chairman said "We have a good program ready for you.

Part one:—Honey as Food in the Bible; by a Groceryman.
Part Two:—Honey as Medicine in the Bible; by a Druggist.

Part Three:—Honey in Cooking, by a Chef,—and finally

Part Four:—Honey as a Symbol of Excellence in the Bible; by the Pastor.

It was an interesting and informative program. The Chairman added:—

There are 42 men here, we had thought there might be 50, so there's plenty for all.

If anyone tumbles up with a tummy-ache we have a Druggist here who will help.

A regular banquet followed.

The honey was gotten out of the Church building North wall near two tiny holes that had been left from some old electric wiring. No man's bees could have made any better honey. Honey is mentioned in the Bible about 22 times.

This is what they said at the banquet.
End of quote.

CROPS DEPENDENT ON BEES FOR POLLINATION : :

Crops Dependent [1]	Crops Increased [2]
Fruit and Nut Crops:	
Almonds	Avocados
Apples - some varieties	Apples - all varieties
Apricots - Riland and Perfection	Bushberries
Cherries, sweet and sour	Macadamia nuts
Chestnuts	Olives - some varieties
Lychee fruit	Pears
Peaches - J.H. Hale, Hal-berta, June Elberta, Candoka and Alamar	Persimmons
Pears - most varieties (Bartletts in un-favorable weather years)	
Plums -European and Japanese	
Prunes	
Tangelos	
Tangerine - Clementine	

Crops Dependent [1]		Crops Increased [2]
Forage Seed Crops:		

Forage Seed Crops:

Crops Dependent [1]	Crops Increased [2]
Alfalfa	Crimson clover
Alsike	
Berseem	
Birdsfoot trefoil	
Sanfoin	
Crown vetch	
Vetch (purple, common hairy)	

Vegetable Seed Crops:

Asparagus	Melons	Eggplant
Broccoli	Onions	Pepper
Brussels sprouts	Parsley	
Cabbage	Parsnips	
Carrots	Pumpkin	
Cauliflower	Radish	
Celery	Rutabaga	
Chinese cabbage	Squash	
Cucumber	Turnip	
Kohlrabi	Watermelon	
Leek		

Vegetable Crops:

Cucumbers	Oil seed crops:
Melons:	Safflower
Cantaloupes	Rape
Honeydews	
Persians	
Watermelons	
Pumpkins	
Squash	

Tree Seed Crops:

Chestnut	Red maple
Catalpa	Yellow poplar
Black locust	Holly

1/ These are unable to produce a commercial crop without cross-pollination.

2/ These generally produce a larger crop when honeybee pollinated.

21.
Earthworms—
For Your Soil & for Your Wealth

O lowly tiller of our soil,
  living in complete obscurity
Laboring more than humans toil
  caring naught for your security.

Yes, they say, you turn. Poor fellow.
  But since God created Adam
You've been here the soil to mellow
  so the food would grow for Madam!

Colonizing by the millions
  by a means a human spurns,
Yet you never danced Cotillions
  nor made use of fire that burns.

Wiggle on, you blessed Plowman.
  if you stop your work, we'd perish.
You won't need Archers or Bowman.
  Drilling holes is what you cherish.

Food is what the living wishes.
  Without food the living die.
You're good food for birds and fishes,
  birds can eat you while they fly.

Nourishing Food won't grow without thee.
  Keep on digging, throw up casts,
Multiply your myriad progeny.
  If you rest, we'll go on fasts.

N.W.W.

   Earthworms have a double value. They are essential in the growing of nourishing food and in changing a sterile worthless soil into a fertile one. That's number one value.

Number two value is the potential financial opportunities from raising earthworms. A whole volume could be published of the untold thousands who have built up an "Earthworms-for-Sale" business from an investment of a mere few dollars, to $100, $500 and into the thousands of dollars a month, either as a part-time hobby or as a full time business.

Earthworms are not only prolific, but they can multiply almost faster than a computer can keep track of them, so to speak. As the earthworms enrich the soil, the richness of the soil contributes to their proliferation.

There is absolutely no comparison between earthworm-conditioned soil and soil which has been repeatedly treated with commercial fertilizers. Earthworm castings have been known to supply 300% more magnesium to the soil, 500% more nitrogen, 700% more phosphorus and more than one thousand percent more potash to the soil than was analyzed in the soil of adjoining farms in which the soil was treated with chemical fertilizers.

Earthworms will supply vast quantities of rich organic fertilizing material. After only 3 or 4 years there may be as many as 1,000,000 to 2,000,000 or more earthworms per acre, producing a rich supply of castings which are an excellent organic fertilizer. These could yield between 1 1/2 and 2 1/2 tons of castings per acre every 24 hours under favorable moist weather conditions, through Spring, Summer and Fall, and even through the Winter if temperatures are right. What a bonanza that is - at virtually no outlay of money.

Once you get your land, your 5 or 10 acre farm, you can get these indefatigable plowmen to work for you 24 hours a day, day in and day out, at no pay, no side or other benefits and no backtalk.

The earthworm is an efficient complex chemical laboratory. It exists in the soil, consumes the soil, and returns the soil fertilized, enriching it. His only requirement is the presence of organic matter in the ground. He digests it together with any decaying vegetation, plant or spores, bacteria eggs, insect eggs and larvae. After digesting all this he expels the residue and deposits it in the form known as CASTS on the surface of the ground. These casts or castings provide a very finely broken down immensely rich fertilizer.

The castings of one earthworm would not go far towards fertilizing a garden or field or a farm, but we have seen how prolific earthworms are and how fast the castings accumulate. Only 75,000 to 1,000,000 earthworms per acre could yield from 45 to more than 75 tons of rich fertilizer per acre a month. With such incontrovertible facts in mind, I fail to understand why any intelligent person would want to use chemical fertilizers and destroy the earthworms already in the soil.

The earthworm drills its way through the earth by swallowing the soil, in this manner making its underground channels. These channels not only serve for its locomotion, but they aerate the ground, open it up, and water can thus penetrate deeply underground.

The late Mr. E.B. Shields published a little 120 page booklet of excellent detailed information on the subject of earthworms entitled RAISING EARTHWORMS FOR PROFIT. As it is hardly within the scope of this book (this, my book) to give you a detailed education on this vitally interesting subject, I suggest you obtain a copy of Mr. Shield's book. I bought my copy many years ago and I see it still advertized by SHIELDS PUBLICATIONS, Box 472, Elgin, Illinois, 60120. You will find therein illustrations on how to proceed with your earthworm anticipated profit and fortune in the chapter headed: "Starting with Propagation Boxes". In his preceding chapter headed "A Miracle of Multiplication" you can estimate the value of his figuring as conservative when he points out the possibility—under the very best conditions—of starting with 1,000 earthworms and ending up at the end of a 2 year breeding period with more than ONE BILLION earthworms, plus about 300 million egg-capsules with a potential content of from 2 or 3 to more than a dozen worms hatchable in each capsule.

Here is something very important for you to consider when finding the country place that appeals to you, only to discover that the ground has either been worked to death or is just plain sterile. This kind of land can usually be bought for a song, yet within one year you could raise enough earthworms to reclaim that land into fertility sufficiently to furnish you with a fair crop of food. In the subsequent years your land would be progressively more fertile than any chemically-treated land in the community.

I get so tremendously enthused when I think of the unlimited possibilities of reclaiming "unusable" land that I am almost tempted to stop typing manuscripts right here and now and get out into the country, - but my good and level-headed wife discourages me. She just has to say to me: "Look at the mail that comes to you from all over the World. You can't let these people down. They want, and they need, the results of your research. Go ahead and concentrate on more books for a while, then we'll see what's best for everyone concerned". What a well-balanced wife I have. So—here I am, working to complete this manuscript.

Whatever system you decide to use for this enterprise, you should have a vegetable and weed grinder, a hammermill, with which to grind everything that grows, finely enough for food for your little pets. Gather the leaves as they fall off the trees and bushes, they are all avidly eaten by earthworms, and the finer they are ground the more readily will the earthworms digest them.

The more sterile soil you have on your place, just that more compost, manure and ground-up trimmings will you need, but by having an abundance of such material your earthworms will multiply to such an extent that your sterile ground will be completely transformed into a rich, crumbly, porous and friable soil.

Keep in mind that an acre can contain with great advantage from a few hundred thousand earthworms to one or 2 million, or more.

ANATOMY OF THE EARTHWORM. Anatomically, the earthworm is one of the most interesting creatures on earth. It has neither eyes nor ears nor teeth. It is sensitive to vibrations and to light, yet it goes to its desired destination with unerring accuracy. It has about 6 hearts - you could never call it heartless! Its smaller end is its mouth and its brain. Yes, indeed, it has a brain. It is equipped with a complete set of both male and female sex organs, but it must have contact with another earthworm to become fertilized.

By the action of its bulb-like esophagus working like a suction pump, it takes into its body whatever organic matter is available, as nourishment. It has a gizzard, somewhat like that of a bird, and it needs microscopic sharp particles of stone, gravel or other solid matter in order to swallow its "food" and the earth, and pass it all through its digestive system.

The earthworm absorbs oxygen and expels it as carbon dioxide through the moist outer covering of its body, hence the need to keep the soil moist. This breathing action can ONLY take place when its outer skin is moist. The earthworm shuns sunlight and dry air because without moisture it dies, hence the need of keeping the soil in which you have earthworms constantly moist, yet not so wet as to drown the poor creatures. You will notice that when there is an excessive amount of rain, enough to flood their underground passages, they wiggle to the surface as fast as possible to keep from drowning.

A healthy earthworm, under favorable conditions, is likely to produce 2,000 to 3,000 offspring a year. That is why, if you can keep them breeding the year round, you could get between 2,000,000 and 3,000,000 earthworms a year. Its average life, under good conditions, is about 15 years. I know of no business or enterprise that can yield such fantastic results.

The earthworm itself is only part of the enterprise. An earthworm ejects its own weight in castings every day. This means an accumulation of 1-to 1 1/4 pounds of the richest fertilizer material, each year, from every earthworm. This doesn't sound like much, but get a few hundred thousand earthworms in one acre and they will throw up from 50 to 400 TONS or more castings every year in that acre. These castings are loaded with nitrogen, potash and phosphate, essential elements for soil build-up.

The burrow which the earthworm creates enables water, rain and irrigation to penetrate deep into the ground, instead of being washed off the surface together with topsoil. These tunnels run deep - as much as 6 to 8 feet below the surface of the ground.

Another important consideration is the fact that when you have an ample stock of earthworms in your soil, you will not need mechanical cultivating machinery. Earthworms do not injure the fine roots the way mechanical cultivation is apt to do. In fact you may get larger crops and in notably greater quantities than by the use of machinery.

If you have hills on your land which you are not cultivating, by all means make it a project to implant as many earthworms on them as you can spare. They will drill and burrow into the hill and the castings which

Our invaluable friends, Earthworms

they throw up will eventually be washed down onto the lower ground by the wind and rain and, in the course of years, will elevate the level of the lower ground.

I emphasize the fact that, due to the practices of the commercial fertilizer enterprises, about 80% of the arable land in the United States of America has been ruined and made less productive, frequently actually sterile, by the nihilistic use of chemical fertilizers and poisonous sprays. Unquestionably the best way that such land can be reclaimed for maximum productivity is by the propagation of vast quantities of earthworms to revitalize the soil with their castings. This will require the production of millions upon millions of earthworms and millions of tons of their castings.

Study the catalogues of real estate and farm agencies and contact as many real estate brokers as possible, and see how many places can be bought for virtually a song. A great many of the places advertized could be bought for one half or less than the asking price. Why? Usually because the soil will not yield a living under the destructive farming methods used.

SO MANY PEOPLE ARE RAISING EARTHWORMS! Many of the WORM FARMS are actually advertising for earthworms which they can buy, because they cannot supply the demand. Many advertise that they will sell earthworms and buy all the surplus which their customers can produce. Already many enterprising people, men and women of all ages, have gone into the business either as a part-time hobby or as a full time business. Is there any reason why YOU cannot do the same? Get Mr. Shield's book to which I have referred in a preceding paragraph, study the possibilities the way he outlines them, and judge for yourself if you are qualified to go into a business which can be highly profitable. Other people have done so. You can do the same.

Start LIVING WITH A PURPOSE!

**Avoid the Depression . . .
move to the real country**

for your food in abundance
for your economic security
for your self-preservation

22.
Enjoying the Life-style of your Dreams. .

Nations and homes are ruined by inflation.
No need for you to court such a disaster.
Preserve your surplus food by dehydration.
While others fret you will recover faster.

A dream come true!—A hobbyshop! Your own!
Now you can work or play, or stop at will,
Or as a Fix-It man, in some small town
Help many other people.—What a thrill!

Just think! A new, completely changed Life-style
With Liberty and Freedom on your own domain,
Unfettered, you can laugh-or smile,
And feel you have not lived your life in vain.

N.W.W.

Do you have the KEY which opens the door to new beginnings? The easiest, most submissive, pliant way to become a mediocre, common-place, insignificant individual is to stay in a RUT and stagnate. Who wants to be a nonentity?

Of course you must understand that the foregoing sentence is NOT meant nor intended for YOU!

The very fact that you have succeeded in reading this book as far as this, proves to me that you ARE definitely interested in the decentralization of the large Metropolitan centers with which our Great United States is plagued, in so far as individuals are concerned.

As I have tried to emphasize earlier in these pages, large Cities are very definitely necessary. But that does not mean that you and I must be condemned to be imprisoned as more or less insignificant units in these Metropolies.

You and I are definitely interested in the matter of constructive self-determination in so far as where we live and what we do is concerned. If we are disturbed by the noise, smog, and other conditions which irritate us and which confront us in the City, then we yearn for the life-giving, invigorating fresh air of the countryside, the blue skies above, the twittering birds around us and the frisky antics of the little denizens of the field and forest.

We are interested in having a garden in which we can grow our own food, organically. A few acres on which we can keep and enjoy Guinea fowl, choice poultry, some of the small Dexter cattle, some pygmy goats, bees for our honey and - above all - enjoy a degree of Liberty and Freedom which it is virtually impossible to obtain in a large City.

The advantages of living out in the country are as multitudinous and innumerable as they are important and vital. To grow your own food, your own fresh vegetables and fruits in such abundance that, besides having a supply after what is needed for meals, there is enough left over to dehydrate for future use and to sell, thus helping your budget.

Your fruit trees should yield crops which are more ample than you can consume while they are at the peak of their ripeness. At their very best, with quality and flavor that is not obtainable in City markets, their surplus is also available for dehydration for future use, and for sale.

Your flock of Guineas are invaluable for their ability to warn you of the approach of anything strange, whether it be a person, a predatory bird or an animal. Their value, both for egg production and for the table, has the advantage of being cheaper both in housing and in feed, than is the cost of raising and keeping poultry.

Your poultry could have tremendous possibilities for being groomed for County and other Fairs, besides their value in reducing the cost of eggs per dozen, particularly if you will grow all or most of their feed. Their market value, preferably to private families, is an excellent source of income if properly handled. Their droppings are an invaluable source of fertilizer for your compost.

Also for the fertilizer, which is so essential in compost, you could have a number of those tiny Irish Dexter cattle which are easy to handle and manage, they are docile and small enough so that several of them can be kept on an amazingly small amount of acreage. Their milk is almost identical to Goats' milk, so that it can be used without the fear of your being afflicted with excessive mucus, as would be the case of milk from the regular cows generally used by dairy farmers. Furthermore, for meat-eaters the flesh of Dexter cattle is better digested than that of larger size cattle and the price obtained for such animals for table use is reported to be very satisfactory, — another addition to your budget.

We must not overlook the little diminutive Goats which grow rarely any higher than 18 to 22 inches at the withers. These have already been clearly described, together with their behavior, antics, etc., in the PYGMY GOATS chapter.

Bees are the pride and joy of nearly all Beekeepers. There is no substitute for the honey from your own bees, honey which you do not dilute, adulterate nor overheat.

All in all, can you think of a greater bonanza than a few acres - or as many as you want - in the wide open country, with the Freedom and Liberty which go with it, with all its advantages? Everything on a Mini-farm can be made productive. If you have enough land, you can grow trees for reforestation. With a Hobby-shop you have all the scope you want to give full play to your skills and ingenuity.

If you are a good all-around Handyman or a Jack of all trades, you could very well build up quite a FIX-IT business which is so much needed in many small communities. You would be surprised to discover how many Farmers wish there were a FIX-IT man available, to replace broken windows or hinges, repair their pumping engines or windmills and even to install lightning rods.

Let me disabuse you of any idea you may have that moving to your Mini-farm is going to be all peaches and cream, that you will have time to spare, time on your hands, easy going. On the contrary. The success you achieve is in direct ratio and commensurate with or to the time, patience, labor and effort that you expend on the project. If this does not phase you, then let's get going.

If you have children, they deserve a great deal more than a mere cursory wishful thinking about going out to the country and living life with a purpose. It is sad to realize that the very basis upon which America has grown to its present day stature, namely the family and its children, has so far deviated from its original practices that America seems to have lost some of the simple values that made it great. The secret of training the children seems to have been generally lost. What was that secret? Simply the ordinary family chores done daily, systematically, under the loving guidance and discipline of the parents. This state of affairs can be remedied more easily by living on your 5 or 10 acres in the country than in any other way I can think of.

23.
In Conclusion

You have now come to the conclusion of this dissertation on LIVING LIFE with a PURPOSE for SURVIVAL.

Naturally, I have no means whatever of knowing if my time and effort have been of any value or benefit to you. It could be said that, because I personally love to live in the country, I just wrote this book in order, as the saying is, to blow off steam, or to give reins to excess energy. Of course if you are in any way acquainted with me you will know that this is not the case.

In the first place, I do LOVE the outdoors - and by that I mean THE COUNTRY. To say I dislike the Metropolitan City and City life is a gross understatement of the fact. I am convinced that Almighty God, our Eternal Creator, intended that we should live in, enjoy, and get the greatest benefit possible from all that COUNTRY LIFE has to offer.

It would be utterly ridiculous for anyone to assume that ALL should desert the City and move to the Country. Comparatively few people are equipped mentally, spiritually and physically to live close to and in tune with Nature, with the company of trees, plants, flowers, bees and the birds, as chosen companions. Most people are gregarious, they are unstable, insecure and irresolute unless they can be close to other people and be around them. Many, of course, are thoroughly socially-minded and the very idea of moving from their environment or entourage, for a new kind of life, a new life-style, in the country, does not appeal to them.

Nevertheless, there are crowds and multitudes who are, consciously or otherwise, waiting for the button to be pressed for them to get started on a trek to the COUNTRY in order to LIVE LIFE with a PURPOSE, for happiness as well as for SURVIVAL. To breathe pure unadulterated air. To find means of nourishing the body with food which is entirely free from toxins and poisons. To discover one's spiritual self with a mind able to search for what City life cannot provide, namely, Liberty, Freedom, Economic Security and the reason and purpose for self-preservation.

Whatever may be your reaction to the contents of this book, I cannot even guess. If you feel so inclined, I will appreciate a few lines from you with an expression of your opinion. With the stacks of mail which reaches me from all over the World it may be quite impossible for me to reply. I have no Secretaries - no, not one. I do ALL my own work, including the typing of my manuscripts (which I usually have to type over again two or three times before I am satisfied with their contents). Be patient and tolerant, therefore, and realize that word from you has been a blessing and an encouraging act which will undoubtedly guide me in my future writings.

If and when you follow the suggestions outlined in this book, and move to God's regenerating and re-invigorating country, please let me know where you are.

Your Author,
Dr. N.W. WALKER.

Epilogue

Praise the Lord! The land is Yours.

What a wonderful feeling to express yourself thus
  When you've bought your few acres and settled this matter.
With no time-clocks to punch nor go through all that fuss,-
  You won't have to put up with others' negative chatter,
This Great U.S.A., with more than 3 million
  600 thousand square miles of land,
With Liberty and Freedom envied by a billion
  Who lack what we have and the will to expand.

My last word of advice, as we each go our way-
  Having studied the wisdom contained in this book-
Look around and you'll find, in this Great U.S.A.,
  Just your place, with a field or some woods or a brook.

Go all over the world-you will do so in vain.
  No country has all that we have in this land.
We have mountain and valley, desert and plain
  And more opportunity on every hand.

For sheer beauty of all things, on earth, in the sky,
  The birds and the bees and all things that fly,
The flowers, the trees and gardens galore-
  There's no better home on the sea or on shore.

Quit chasing a rainbow which does not endure.
  On 5 or 10 acres you'll get a supply
Of good food and exercise, air that is pure
  And Health you can build up, but never can buy.

Here in the Country you Can live your life
  With liberty and freedom you cannot disdain.
Your work will be fruitful, without all the strife
  That accompanies climbing for fortune-in vain.

                                        N.W.W.

Index

Fresh Vegetables And Fruit Juices

In FRESH VEGETABLES AND FRUIT JUICES, R. D. Pope, M.D., writes–"Dr. Walker has, for the first time in history, written a complete guide of the Therapeutic uses of our more common, every-day vegetables when taken in the form of fresh, raw juices. It will be of considerable help to those who wish to derive the utmost benefit from the natural foods which God created for the nourishment of Man." Dr. Walker categorically lists vegetable juices, explains their elements, and in cooperation with Doctor Pope, provides suggestions for effective treatment of special ailments.

Colon Health:
The Key To A Vibrant Life

In COLON HEALTH Dr. Walker will take this forgotten part of your body and focus your full attention on it–and you'll never again take it for granted! This books shows how every organ, gland and cell in the body is affected by the condition of the large intestine–the colon. COLON HEALTH answers such questions as: Are cathartics and laxatives dangerous? Can colon care prevent heart attack?–Is your eyesight affected by the condition of your colon?–What are the ghastly results of a colostomy?

Vegetarian Guide To Diet And Salad

The pitfalls of overindulgence in certain food elements, especially oil and sugar, have been well documented. Dr. Walker offers in his book DIET & SALAD both a cook book and a nutritional guide that belongs in every homemaker's kitchen. In it he supports current medical research about the harmful effects of milk–"It is generally assumed that cow's milk is one of our most perfect foods... Milk is the most mucus forming food in the human dietary, and it is the most insidious cause of colds, flu, bronchial troubles, asthma, hay fever, pneumonia, and sinus trouble... cow's milk was never intended for a human infant."

Water Can Undermine Your Health

Dr. Walker sees water pollution as a cause of arthritis, varicose veins, cancer, and even heart attacks–a major problem in virtually every community in the country. His treatment of water pollution is revealing, comprehensive, and scientific. His findings, and his recommendations for corrective action, offer new hope.

Educational Wall Charts

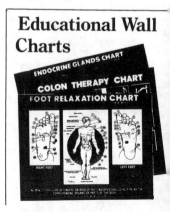

Become Younger

BECOME YOUNGER might be called the "cornerstone" of the famous Walker Program. What place has nutrition in the scheme of good health? How can the body and mind be so tuned that "old age" might be defeated? Dr. Walker suggests "When we embark on this program which may change our eating, drinking and living habits, we must have the courage of our convictions based on the knowledge which we can acquire through the principles involved in this program... To "become younger" means to have attained a state of sublime *self-reliance* and *self-sufficiency which no one can take away from us."*

The Natural Way To Vibrant Health

PROPER NUTRITION IS TANTAMOUNT TO GOOD HEALTH. One man today is walking proof of all this. Dr. NORMAN W. WALKER, a living example of VIBRANT HEALTH, has had the answer since 1910. His information is timeless. The originator of "juice therapy," he made this statement in the preface to one of his books: "The lack or deficiency of certain elements, such as vital organic minerals and salts, and consequently of vitamins, from our customary diet is the primary cause of nearly every sickness and disease." For three quarters of a century MEDICAL EVIDENCE HAS NOT REFUTED HIM.

Natural Weight Control

In NATURAL WEIGHT CONTROL, Dr. Walker offers "A Diet Like No Other"– based on the body's need for vital, life-giving enzymes found only in nature's pure foods. On enzymes he writes– "Enzymes are not things or substances! They are the life-principle in the atoms and molecules of every living cell. The enzymes in the cells of the human body are exactly like those in vegetation, and the atoms in the human body each have a corresponding affinity for like atoms in vegetation."

Easy Weight Control with NEW FOOD COMBINING PLAN

ENDOCRINE GLAND - See where they are located - their innumerable functions, what elements compose them, what Juices nourish them.

COLON THERAPY - A most complete chart of the human Colon. It indicates the relation of nerve endings from head to foot registered in the Colon, and should alert you to study your own condition and do something about it.

FOOT RELAXATION - The soles of your Feed can help relax tension in various parts of your body. This chart shows the Zones on the Soles of the Feet in relationship to the rest of your body.

"x 22" — IN COLOR

Back To The Land For Self-Preservation

In BACK TO THE LAND Dr. Walker examines urban life. His years of working for better health and nutrition have enabled him to see that now is the time to really come to grips with this dilemma.
He offers inspirational thoughts on living your life with a purpose, and "Enjoying the Life-Style of Your Dreams."

INFORMATION REQUEST & ORDER FORM

 **Norwalk** PRESS

107 NORTH CORTEZ
SUITE 200
PRESCOTT, AZ 86301

Date _____

| NAME | _____ |

STREET ADDRESS _____

CITY _____

STATE _____ ZIP _____

QTY.	TITLE	PRICE	TOTAL
	Diet and Salad - Vegetarian Guide to	$5.95	
	Fresh Vegetables and Fruit Juices	$5.95	
	Vibrant Health - the Natural Way to	$5.95	
	Water Can Undermine Your Health	$4.95	
	Become Younger	$5.95	
	Back To The Land for Self-Preservation	$4.95	
	Colon Health: The Key To A Vibrant Life	$5.95	
	Weight Control, Pure and Simple	$5.95	
	Endocrine Chart	$5.00	
	Foot Relaxation Chart	$5.00	
	Colon Therapy Chart	$5.00	

– POSTAGE CHART –
☐ 4th Class Mail - Add $1.25 Per Item
☐ 1st Class / U.P.S. - Add $1.75 Per Item

Sub-Total	$	
Items X $_____ Per Item	$	
TOTAL AMOUNT	$	

Enclosed is my: ☐ Check ☐ Money Order

ALL ORDERS SHIPPED SAME DAY AS RECEIVED
- FOREIGN ORDERS: U.S. FUNDS - MONEY ORDER -

FREE INFORMATION

On services and items suggested or mentioned in Dr. Walker books, please check items you are interested in:*

☐ IN-HOME **DETOXIFICATION Program**

☐ HOME **COLONIC EQUIPMENT**

☐ HOME **VEGETABLE JUICERS**

☐ **WATER DISTILLERS**

☐ HOME **FOOD DEHYDRATORS**

Dr. Walker has no financial interest in any service or product mentioned in his books.

Year after year Modern Medical Science continues to prove...Dr. Walker is right.

INFORMATION REQUEST & ORDER FORM

107 NORTH CORTEZ
SUITE 200
PRESCOTT, AZ 86301

Date _____

| NAME | _____ |

STREET ADDRESS _____

CITY _____

STATE _____ ZIP _____

QTY.	TITLE	PRICE	TOTAL
	Diet and Salad - Vegetarian Guide to	$5.95	
	Fresh Vegetables and Fruit Juices	$5.95	
	Vibrant Health - the Natural Way to	$5.95	
	Water Can Undermine Your Health	$4.95	
	Become Younger	$5.95	
	Back To The Land for Self-Preservation	$4.95	
	Colon Health: The Key To A Vibrant Life	$5.95	
	Weight Control, Pure and Simple	$5.95	
	Endocrine Chart	$5.00	
	Foot Relaxation Chart	$5.00	
	Colon Therapy Chart	$5.00	

— POSTAGE CHART —
☐ 4th Class Mail - Add $1.25 Per Item
☐ 1st Class / U.P.S. - Add $1.75 Per Item

Sub-Total $ _____

_____ Items X $_____ Per Item $ _____

Enclosed is my: ☐ Check ☐ Money Order **TOTAL AMOUNT** $ _____

ALL ORDERS SHIPPED SAME DAY AS RECEIVED
- FOREIGN ORDERS: U.S. FUNDS - MONEY ORDER -

FREE INFORMATION

On services and items suggested or mentioned in Dr. Walker books, please check items you are interested in:*

IN-HOME
☐ DETOXIFICATION Program

HOME
☐ COLONIC EQUIPMENT

HOME
☐ VEGETABLE JUICERS

☐ WATER DISTILLERS

HOME
☐ FOOD DEHYDRATORS

*Dr. Walker has no financial interest in any service or product mentioned in his books.

Year after year Modern Medical Science continues to prove...Dr. Walker is right.